budgetbooks

BROADWAY SONGS

Exclusive Distributors:
Music Sales Limited
8/9 Frith Street, London W1D 3JB, UK.

Order No. HLE90002627
ISBN 1-84609-348-1
This book © Copyright 2006 by Hal Leonard Europe

Printed in the USA

Your Guarantee of Quality
As publishers, we strive to produce every book to the highest commercial standards.
The book has been carefully designed to minimise awkward page turns and to make playing from it a real pleasure.
Throughout, the printing and binding have been planned to ensure a sturdy, attractive publication which should give years of enjoyment.
If your copy fails to meet our high standards, please inform us and we will gladly replace it.

www.musicsales.com

This publication is not authorised for sale in the
United States of America and/or Canada

Hal Leonard Europe
Distributed by Music Sales

CONTENTS

ALL GOOD GIFTS

from the Musical GODSPELL

Words and Music by
STEPHEN SCHWARTZ

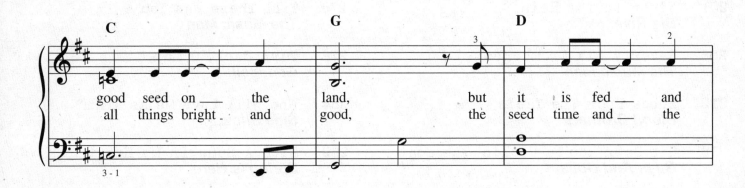

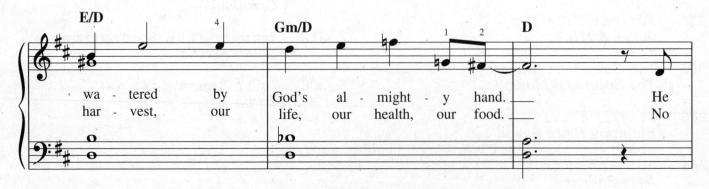

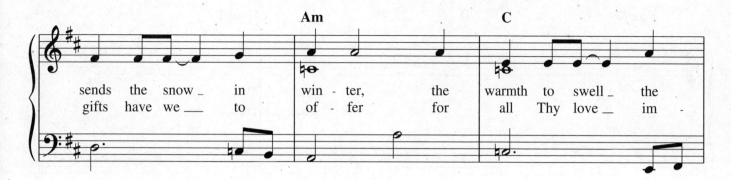

sends the snow ___ in / winter, / the / warmth to swell ___ the
gifts have we ___ to / of - fer / for / all Thy love ___ im -

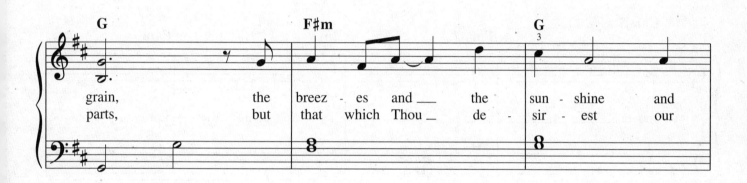

grain, / the / breez - es and ___ the / sun - shine and
parts, / but / that which Thou ___ de - sir - est and our

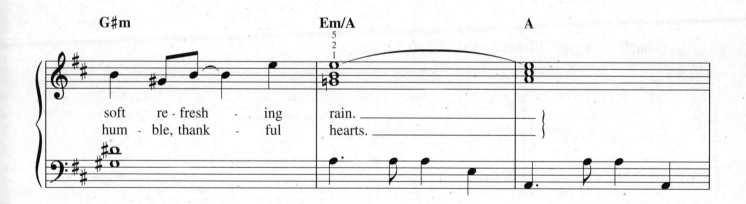

soft re - fresh - ing / rain. _____
hum - ble, thank - ful / hearts. _____

All / good / gifts / a - round ___ us

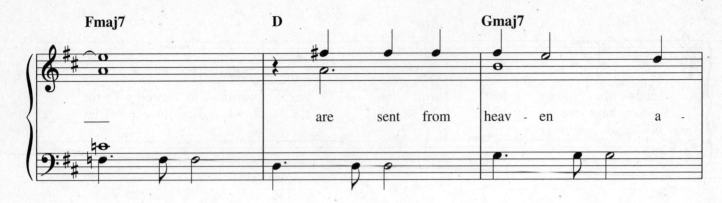

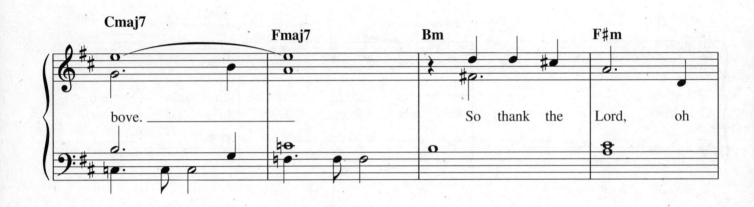

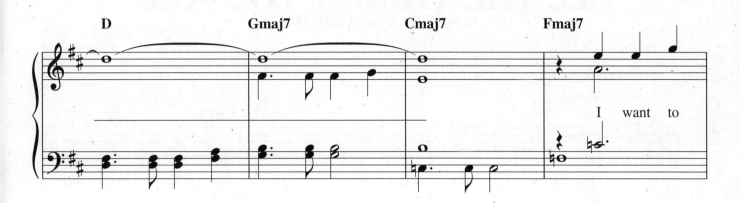

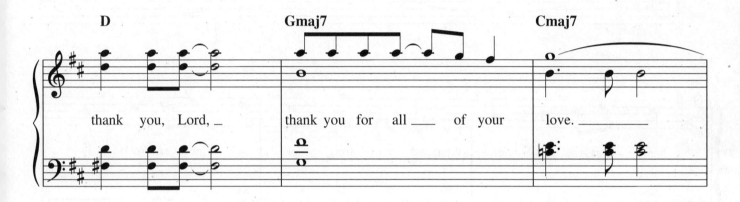

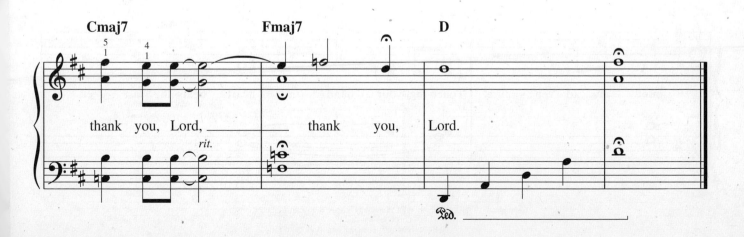

ALL THE THINGS YOU ARE

from VERY WARM FOR MAY

Lyrics by OSCAR HAMMERSTEIN II
Music by JEROME KERN

Freely

Verse

Time and a - gain I've longed for ad - ven - ture, Some-thing to make my

heart beat the fast - er. What did I long for? I nev - er real - ly

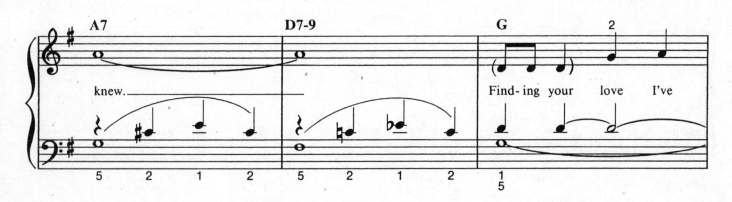

knew. Find - ing your love I've

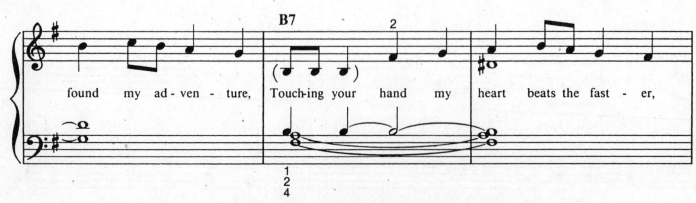

found my ad - ven - ture, Touch-ing your hand my heart beats the fast - er,

Bm7 **Em7** **Am7** **D7** **G**

All that I want in all of this world is you.

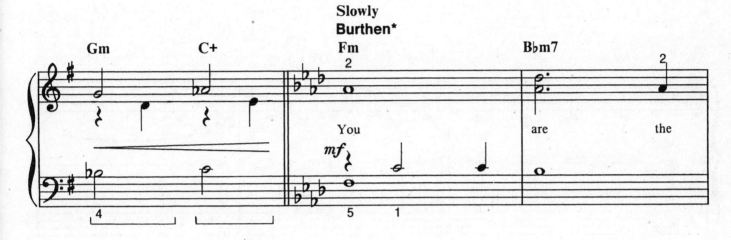

Gm **C+**

Slowly
Burthen*

Fm **Bbm7**

mf

You are the

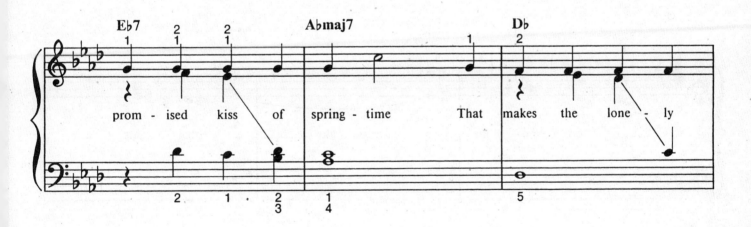

Eb7 **Abmaj7** **Db**

prom - ised kiss of spring - time That makes the lone - ly

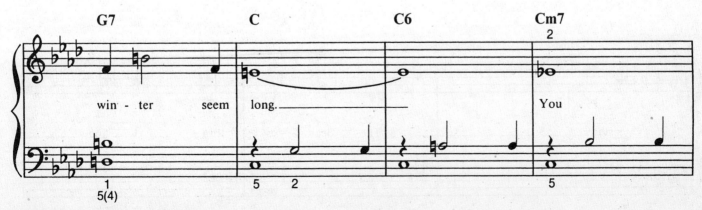

G7 **C** **C6** **Cm7**

win - ter seem long._____ You

*Burthen is another word for chorus.

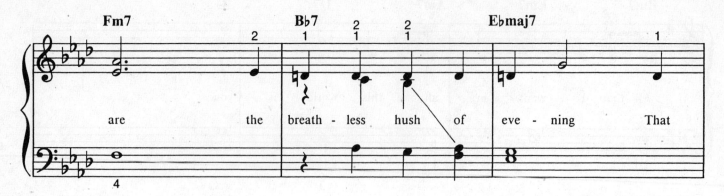

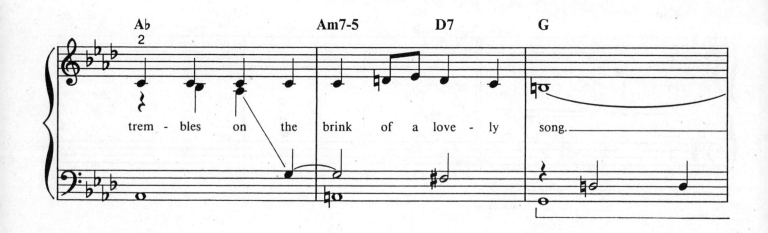

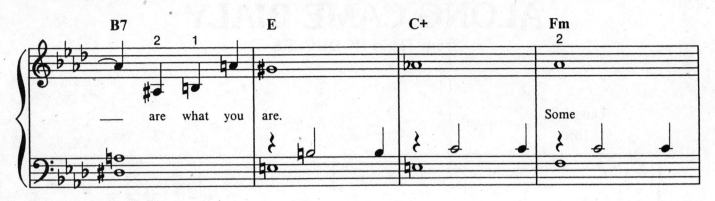

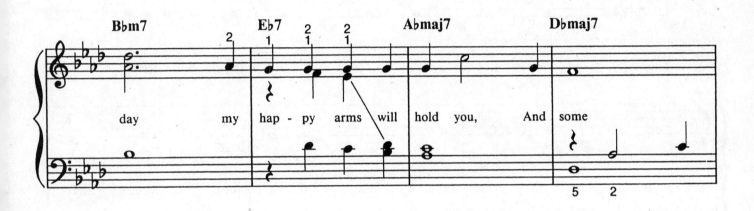

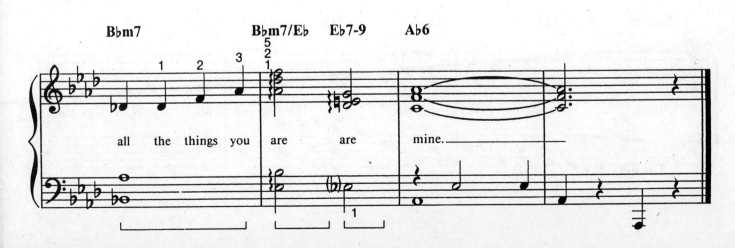

ALONG CAME BIALY
from THE PRODUCERS

Music and Lyrics by
MEL BROOKS

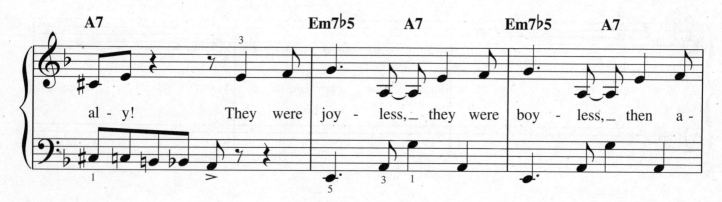

dev - il,___ and I keep those em - bers a - glow.___ When I

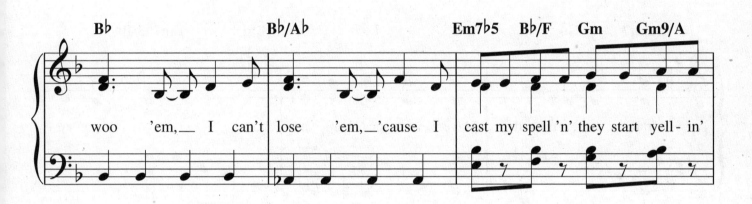

woo 'em,___ I can't lose 'em,___'cause I cast my spell 'n' they start yell - in'

fire down be - low! They were list - ing,___ they were sink - ing,___ then a-

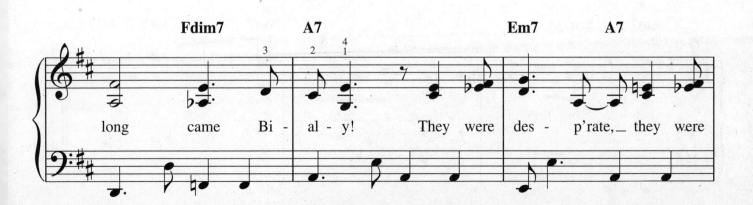

long came Bi - al - y! They were des - p'rate,___ they were

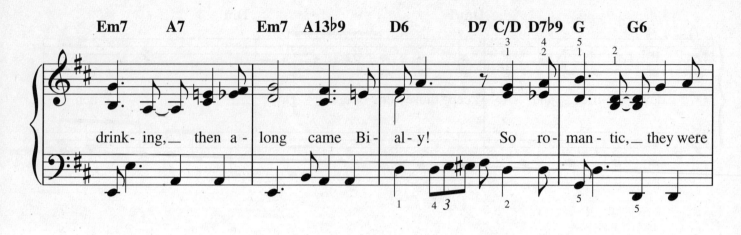

Em7　　A7　　　Em7　A13♭9　　D6　　　D7 C/D D7♭9 G　　G6

drink - ing,__ then a - long came Bi - al - y! So ro - man - tic,__ they were

Gmaj7　　G6　　　　G　　F#7　　　Bm　　Em7♭5/B♭

fran - tic,__ then their prayers were heard up a - bove. Heav - en

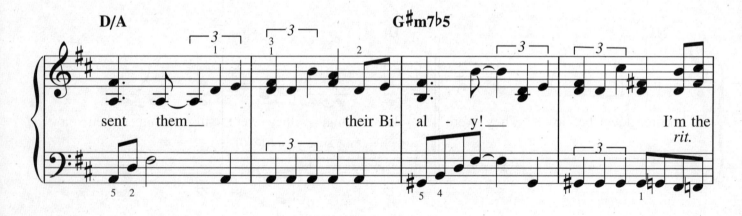

D/A　　　　　　　　　　G#m7♭5

sent them__ their Bi - al - y!__ I'm the
rit.

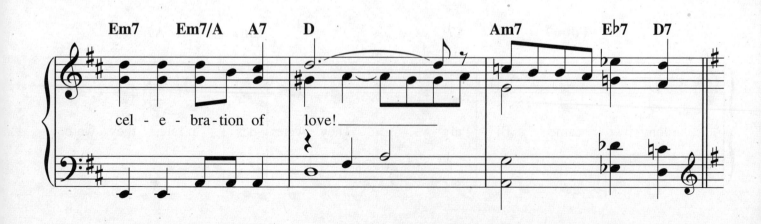

Em7　Em7/A　A7　D　　　　Am7　E♭7　D7

cel - e - bra - tion of love!__

Moderately, in 4
SOLO 1:

Life had passed us by and love had sto - len a - way. At the

Melody in left hand

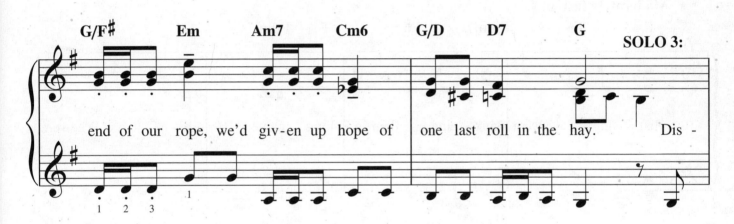

end of our rope, we'd giv-en up hope of one last roll in the hay. Dis -

ALL 3:

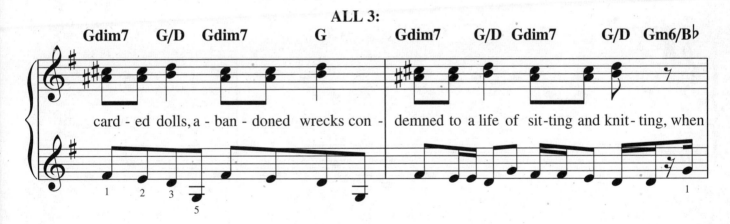

card - ed dolls, a - ban - doned wrecks con - demned to a life of sit-ting and knit-ting, when

Faster, in 4

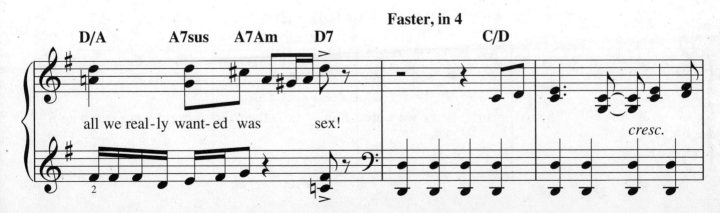

all we real-ly want-ed was sex!

cresc.

LITTLE OLD LADIES:

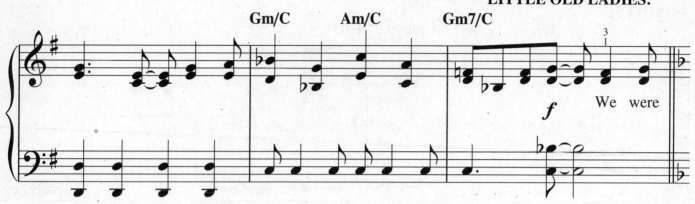

Moderately fast, in 4

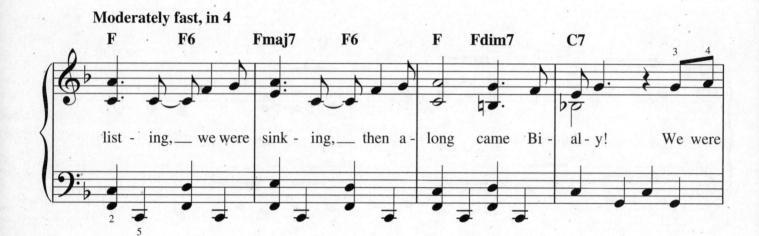

list - ing, __ we were sink - ing, __ then a - long came Bi - al - y! We were

des - p'rate __ we were drink - ing __ then a - long came Bi -

al - y! So ro - man - tic, __ we were fran - tic, __ then our prayers were heard up a -

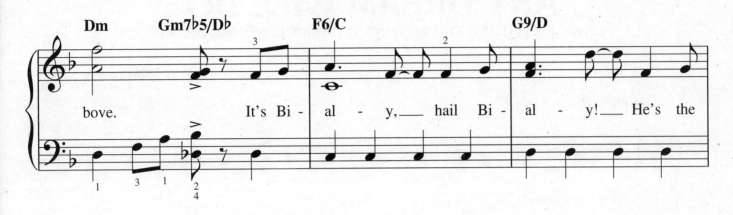

Dm   **Gm7♭5/D♭**   **F6/C**   **G9/D**

bove.   It's Bi - al - y,___ hail Bi - al - y!___ He's the

Gm9/C

cul - min - na - tion,   the   re - sto - ra - tion,   the   con - sum - ma - tion,   the

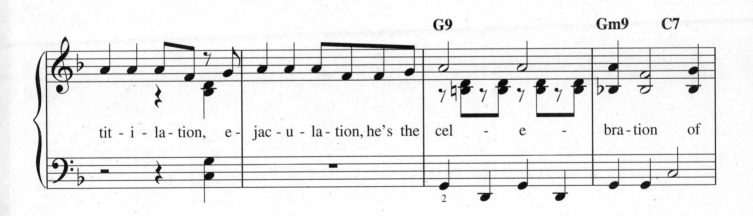

G9   **Gm9**   **C7**

tit - i - la - tion, e - jac - u - la - tion, he's the   cel - e - bra - tion of

F6   **B♭9**   **F6**

love! _____

ANY DREAM WILL DO

from JOSEPH AND THE AMAZING TECHNICOLOR® DREAMCOAT

Music by ANDREW LLOYD WEBBER
Lyrics by TIM RICE

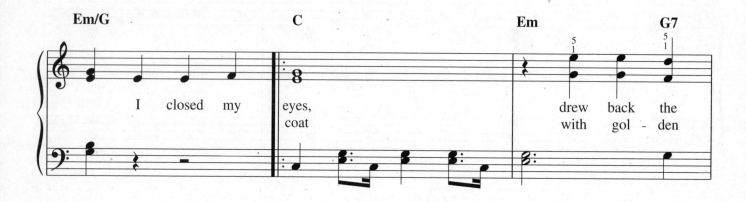

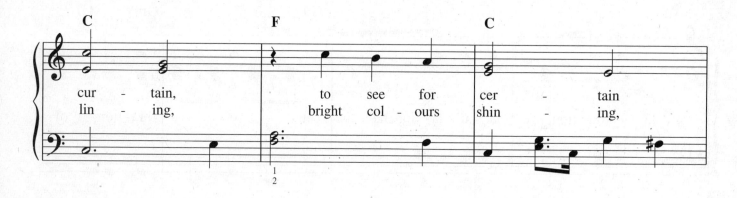

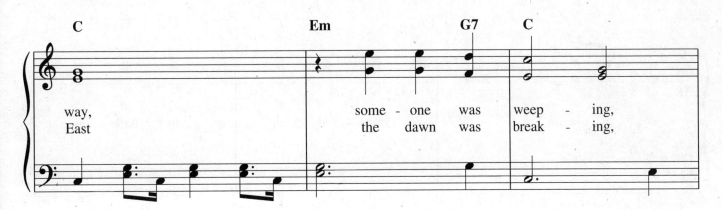

way,
East

some - one was weep - ing,
the dawn was break - ing,

but the world was sleep - ing.
the __ world was wak - ing.

An - y dream will
An - y dream will

1.

do.

I wore my do.

A

crash of drums,__ a flash of light,__ my gol - den coat flew

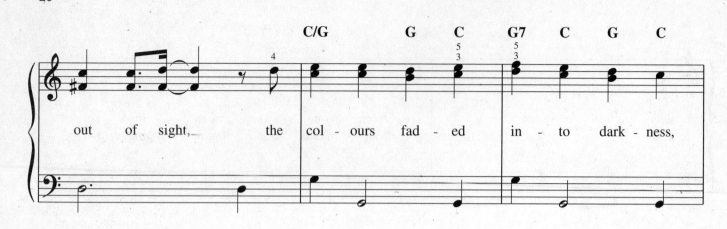

out of sight,___ the col - ours fad - ed in - to dark - ness,

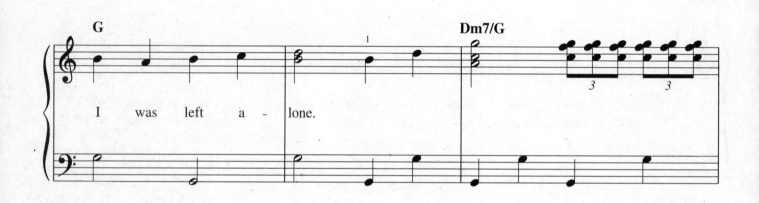

I was left a - lone.

May I re - turn to the be - gin - ning,

The light is dim - ming and the dream is

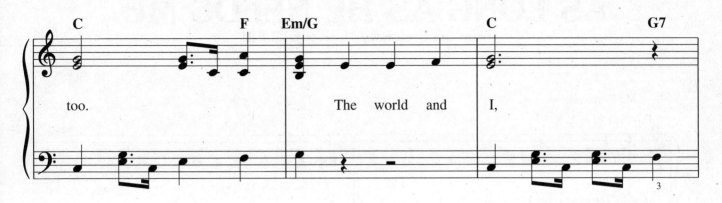

too. The world and I,

we are still wait - ing, still hes - i -

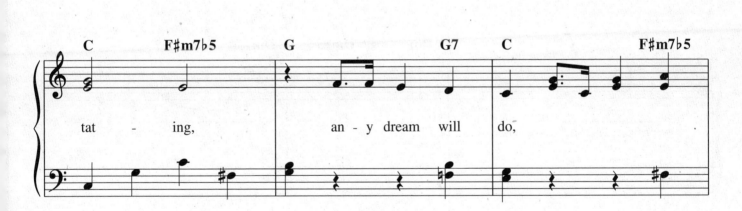

tat - ing, an - y dream will do,

an - y dream will do.

AS LONG AS HE NEEDS ME
from the Broadway Musical OLIVER!

Words and Music by
LIONEL BART

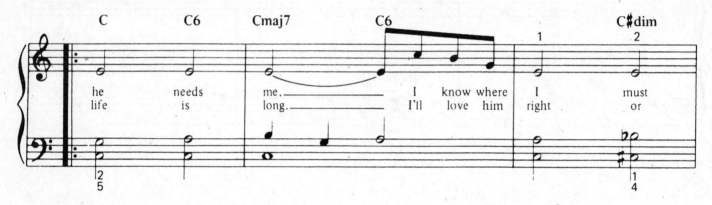

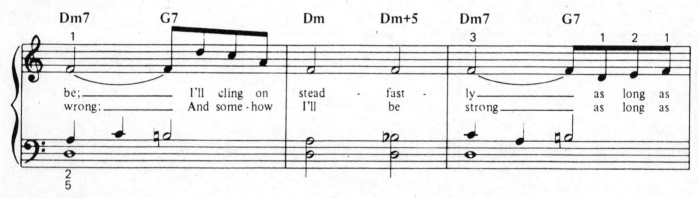

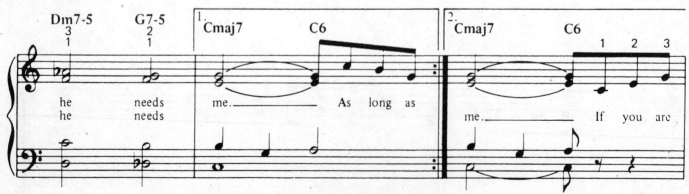

lone - ly_____ then you will know_____ When some-one needs you,_____ you love them

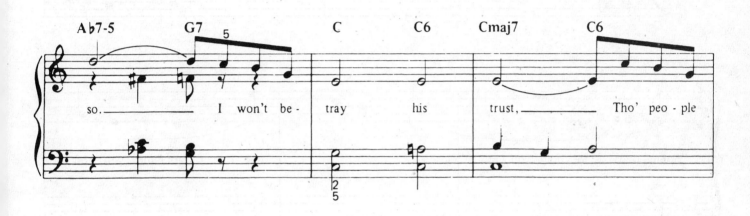

so._____ I won't be - tray his trust,_____ Tho' peo - ple

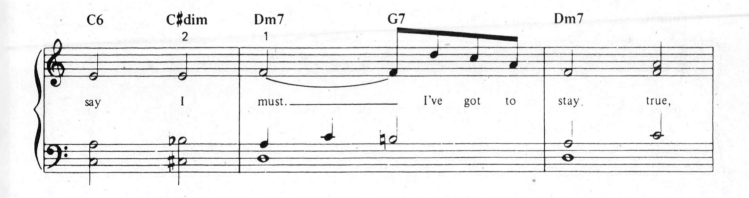

say I must._____ I've got to stay true,

just_____ as long as he needs me.

BEING ALIVE
from COMPANY

Words and Music by
STEPHEN SONDHEIM

Slowly and Freely

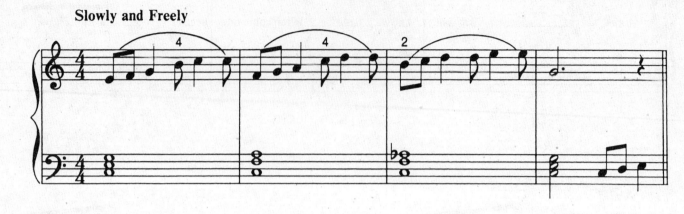

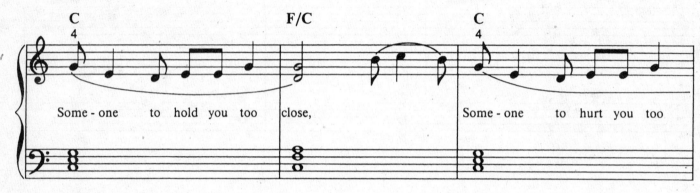

Some-one to hold you too close, Some-one to hurt you too

deep, Some-one to sit in your chair And ru-in your

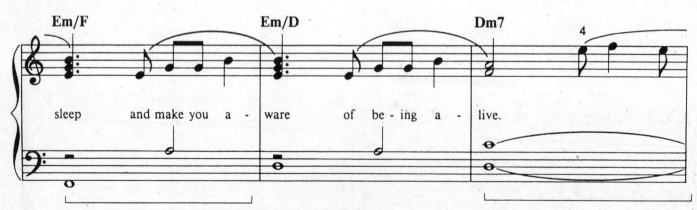

sleep and make you a-ware of be-ing a-live.

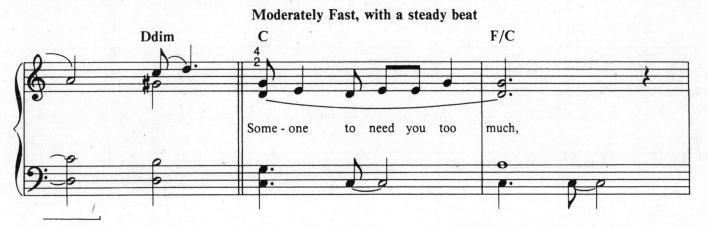

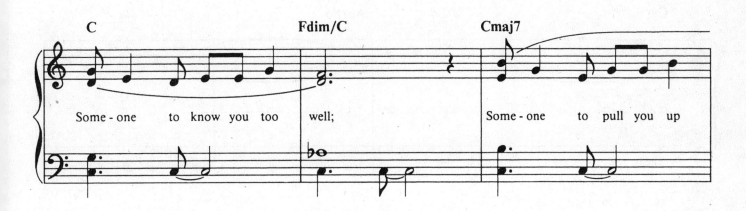

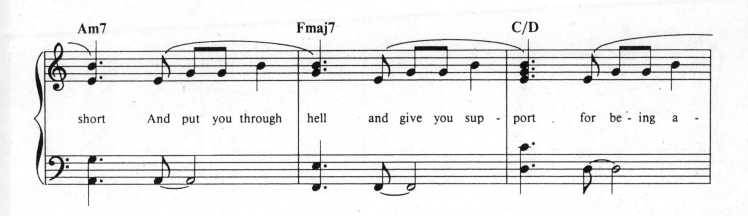

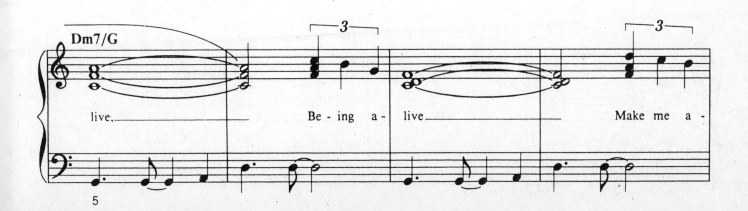

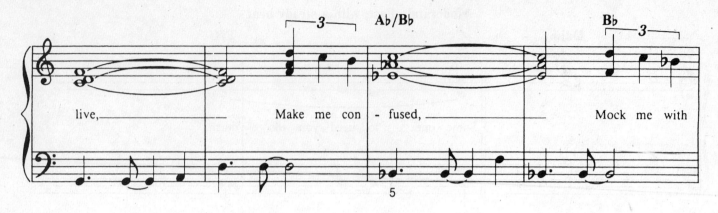

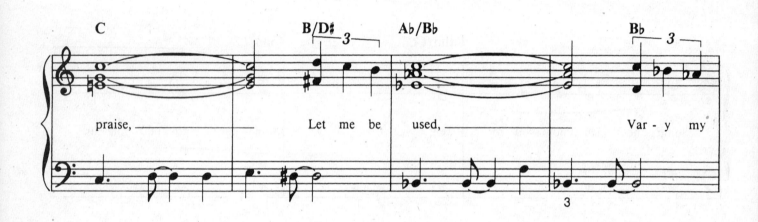

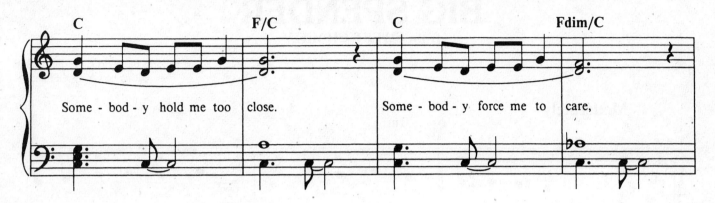

Some - bod - y hold me too close. Some - bod - y force me to care,

Some - bod - y make me come through, I'll al - ways be there as fright - ened as you of be - ing a -

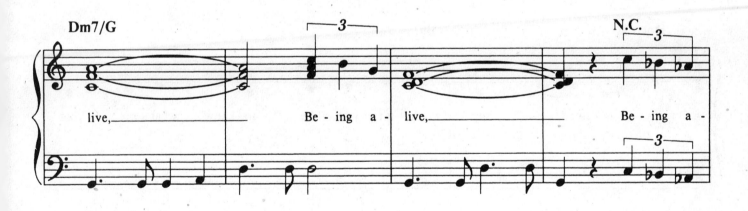

live, _____ Be - ing a - live, _____ Be - ing a -

live.

BIG SPENDER

from SWEET CHARITY

Words by DOROTHY FIELDS
Music by CY COLEMAN

BROADWAY BABY

from FOLLIES

Words and Music by
STEPHEN SONDHEIM

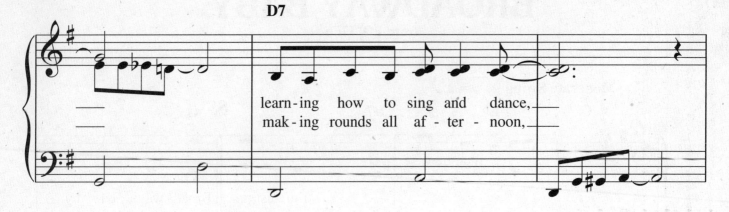

learn-ing how to sing and dance,_____
mak-ing rounds all af - ter - noon,_____

wait - ing for that one big chance_____ to be in a
eat - ing at a greas - y spoon_____ to save on my

show._____
dough._____

Gee, I'd like to
At my ti - ny

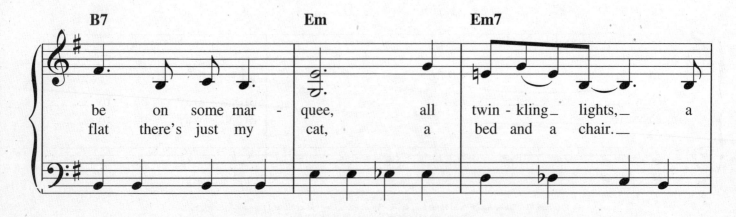

be on some mar - quee, all twin - kling_ lights,_ a
flat there's just my cat, a bed and a chair._

C7

Say, Mis - ter Pro - duc - er,

G7

I'm talk - ing to you, sir.

D7

I don't need a lot, on - ly what I got,

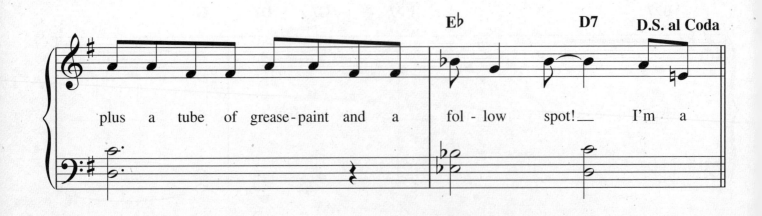

Eb **D7** **D.S. al Coda**

plus a tube of grease-paint and a fol - low spot!__ I'm a

CODA

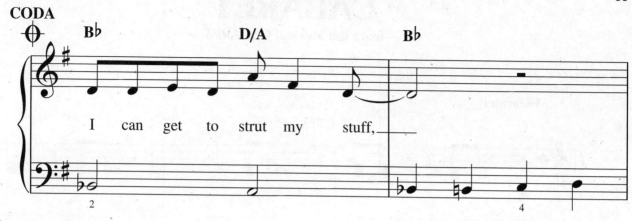

I can get to strut my stuff,

work-ing for a nice man like a Zieg-feld or a Weiss-man in a

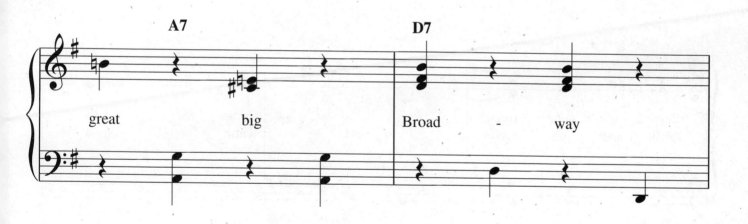

great big Broad - way

show!

CABARET
from the Musical CABARET

Words by FRED EBB
Music by JOHN KANDER

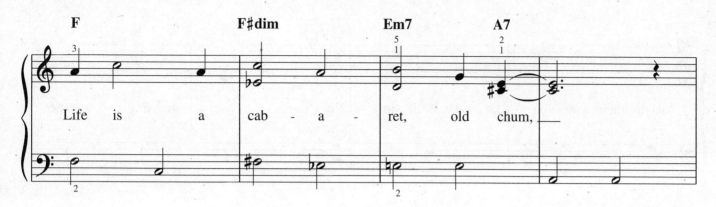

Life is a cab - a - ret, old chum,

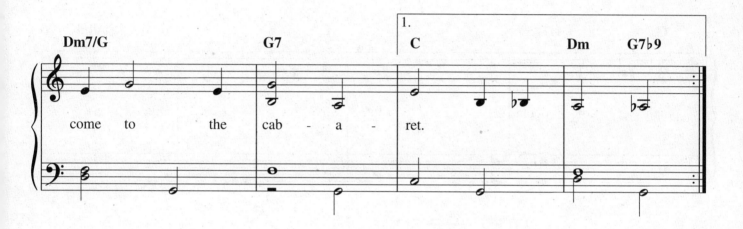

come to the cab - a - ret.

ret. Come taste the wine, come hear the

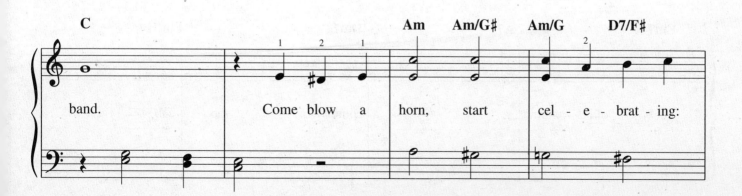

band. Come blow a horn, start cel - e - brat - ing:

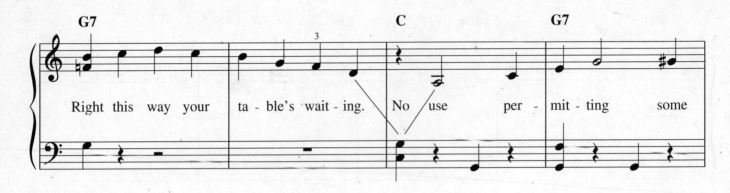

Right this way your ta - ble's wait - ing. No use per - mit - ting some

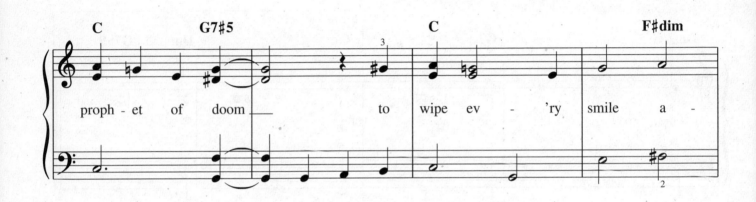

proph - et of doom ___ to wipe ev - 'ry smile a -

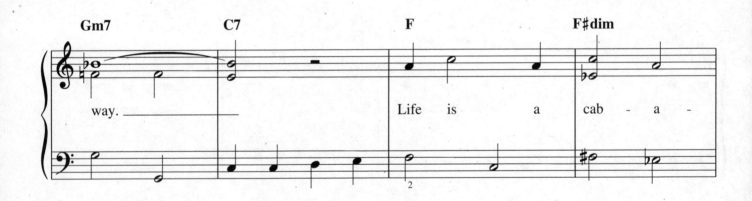

way. ___ Life is a cab - a -

ret, old chum, ___ come to the cab - a -

Slightly faster

ret! I

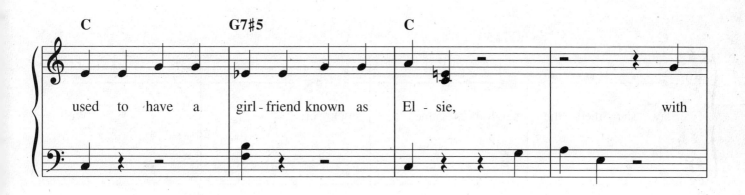

used to have a girl - friend known as El - sie, with

whom I shared four sor - did rooms in Chel - sea. She

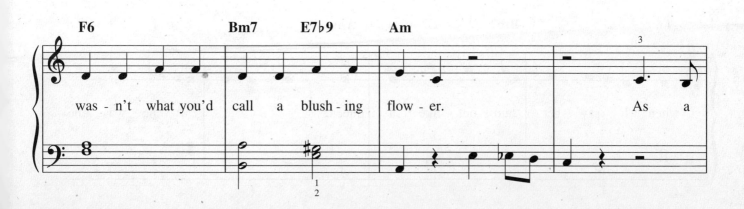

was - n't what you'd call a blush - ing flow - er. As a

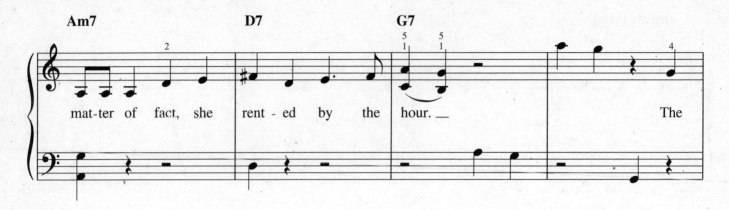

mat-ter of fact, she rent-ed by the hour. ___ The

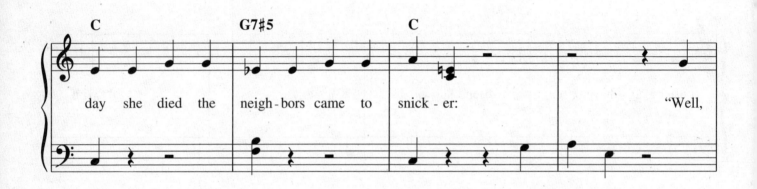

day she died the neigh-bors came to snick - er: "Well,

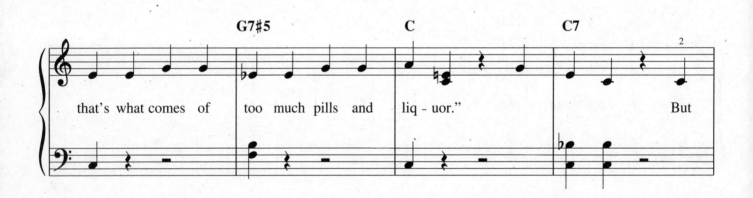

that's what comes of too much pills and liq - uor." But

when I saw her laid out like a queen, she was the

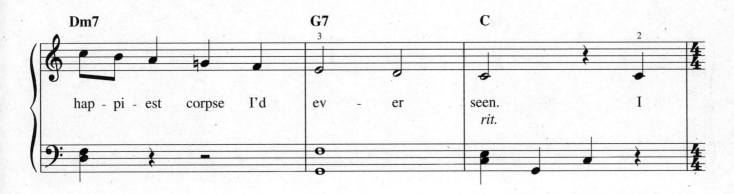

hap - pi - est corpse I'd ev - er seen. I

think of El - sie to this ver - y day. I re -

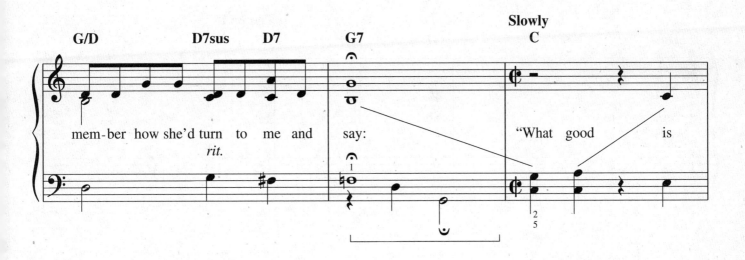

mem - ber how she'd turn to me and say: "What good is

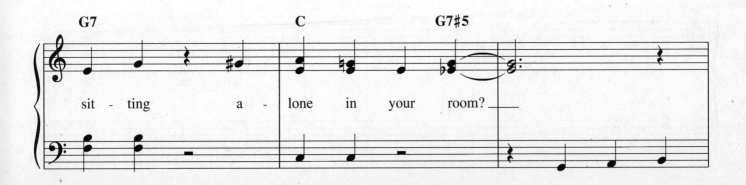

sit - ting a - lone in your room?

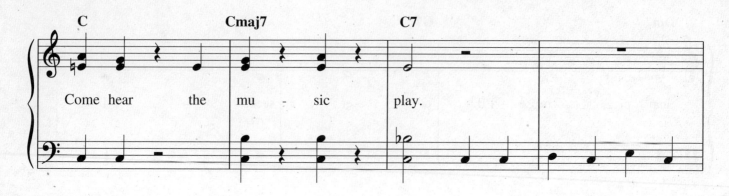

Come hear the mu - sic play.

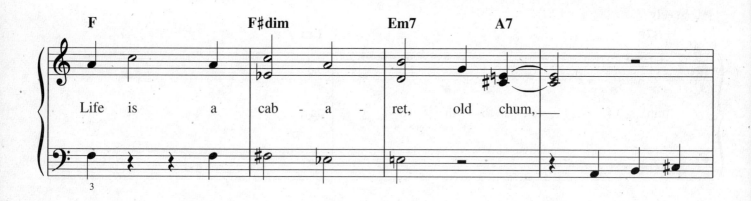

Life is a cab - a - ret, old chum,

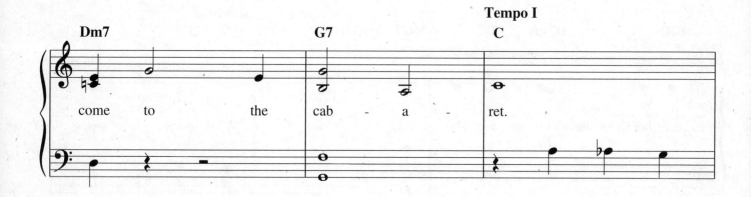

come to the cab - a - ret.

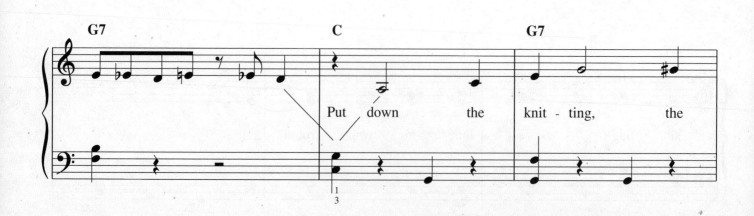

Put down the knit - ting, the

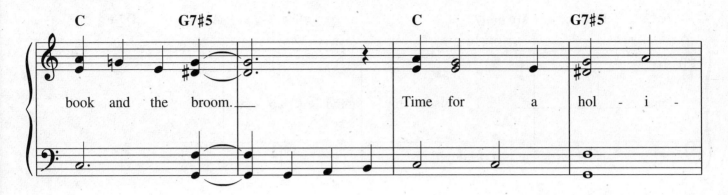

book and the broom.___ Time for a hol - i -

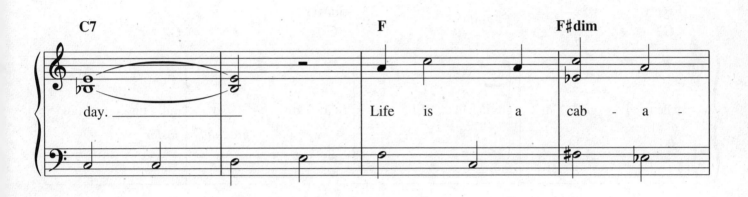

day.___ Life is a cab - a -

ret, old chum,___ come to the cab - a -

ret." And as for me,___ as for

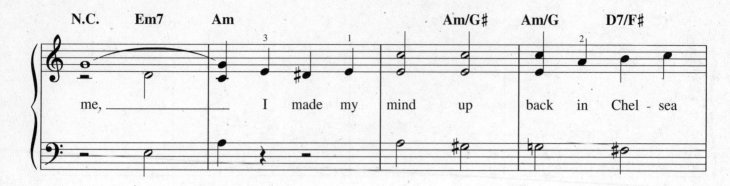

N.C.   **Em7**   **Am**   **Am/G#**   **Am/G**   **D7/F#**

me, _____ I made my mind up back in Chel - sea

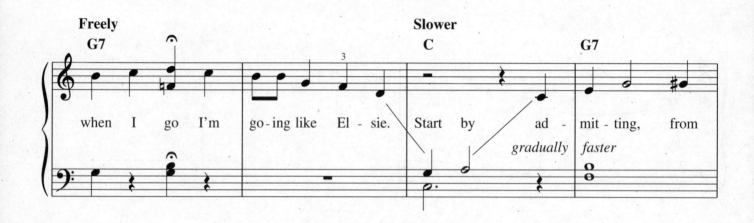

Freely
G7   **Slower**
            C   **G7**

when I go I'm go-ing like El - sie. Start by ad - mit - ting, from

gradually   *faster*

C   **G7#5**   **C**

cra - dle to tomb __ is - n't that long a

Tempo I
Gm7   **C7**   **F**   **F#dim**

stay.   Life is a cab - a -

gradually faster

ret,　　old　chum,　　　　　　on - ly　　a　　cab - a -

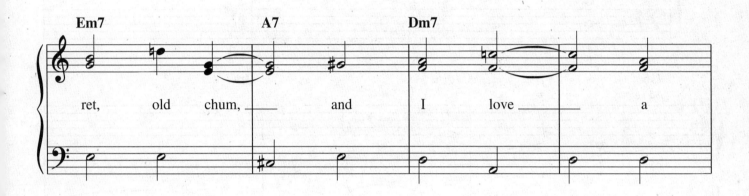

ret,　　old　chum,　　　　　and　　I　　love　　　　　a

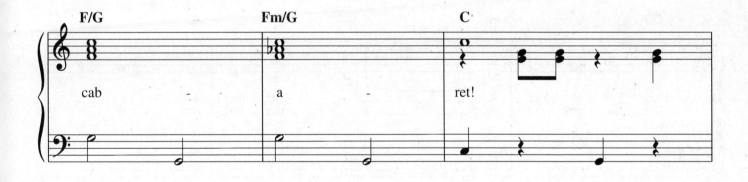

cab　-　　a　-　　ret!

46

A COCK-EYED OPTIMIST
from SOUTH PACIFIC

Lyrics by OSCAR HAMMERSTEIN II
Music by RICHARD RODGERS

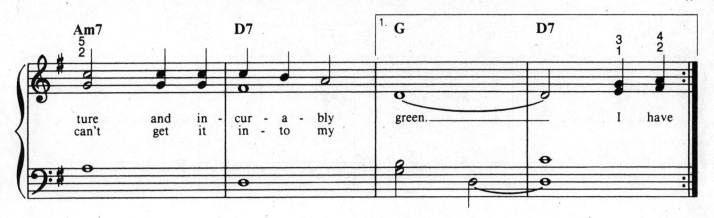

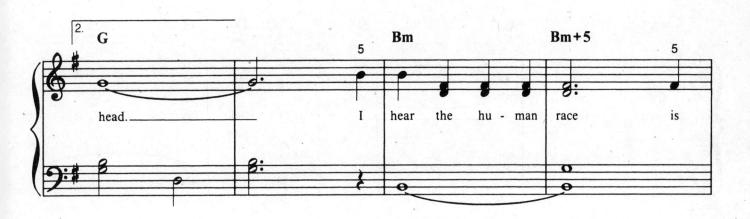

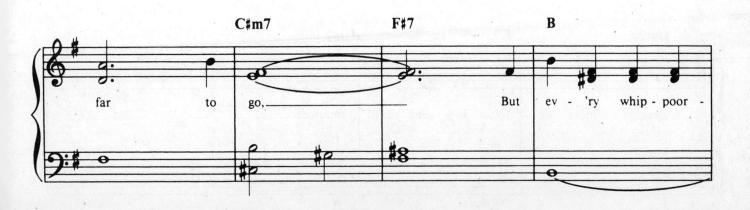

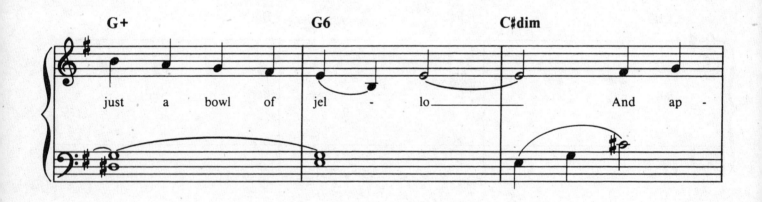

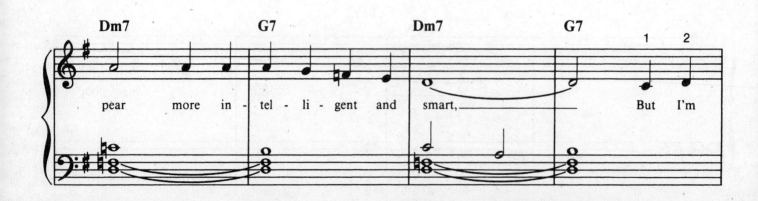

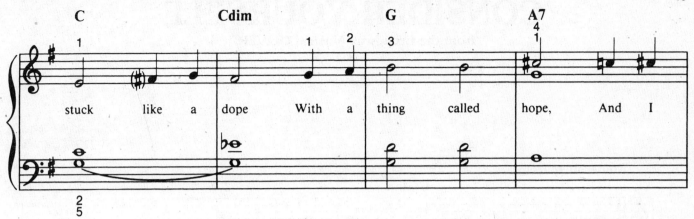

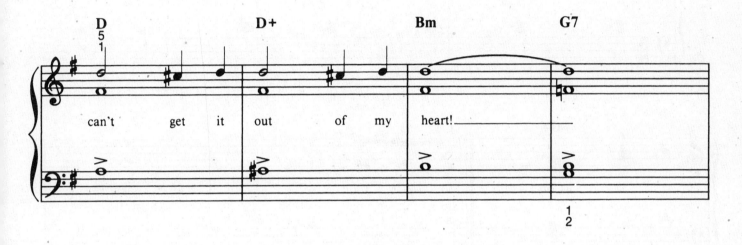

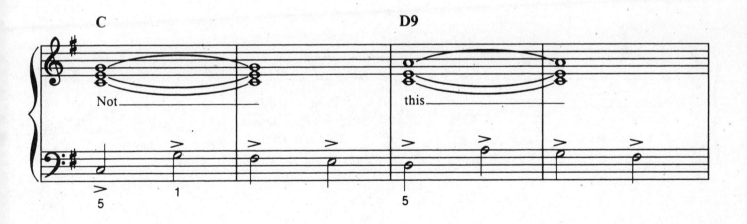

CONSIDER YOURSELF

from the Broadway Musical OLIVER!

Words and Music by
LIONEL BART

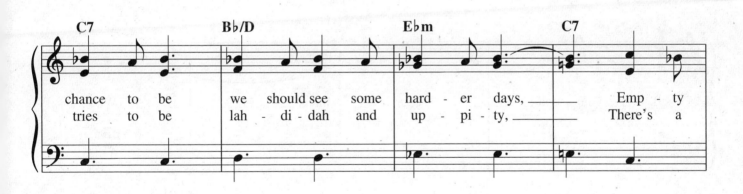

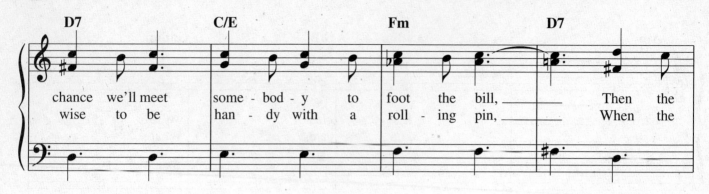

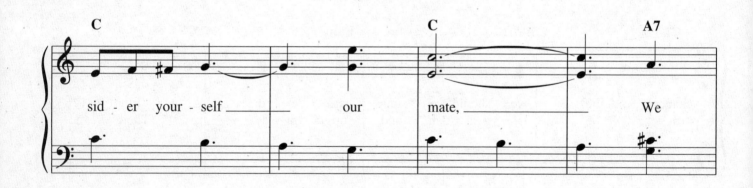

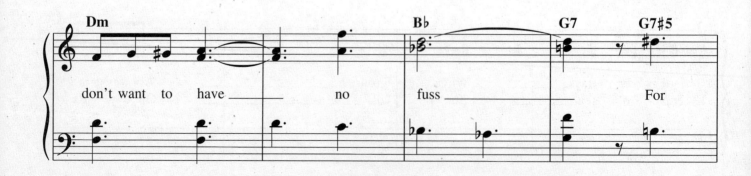

af - ter some con - sid - er - a - tion, we can state: Con -

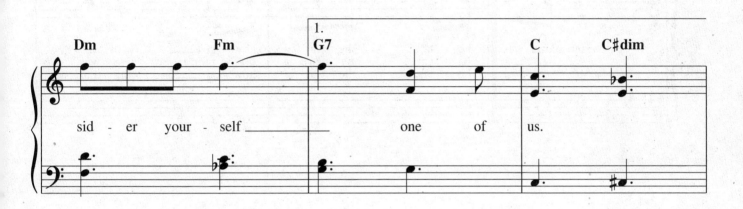

sid - er your - self _____ one of us.

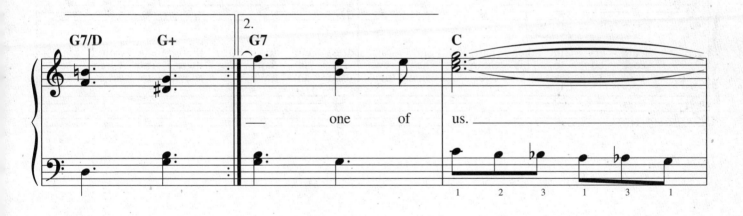

___ one of us. _____

COPACABANA

(At The Copa)
from Barry Manilow's COPACABANA

Music by BARRY MANILOW
Lyric by BRUCE SUSSMAN and JACK FELDMAN

Moderately, with a Latin "feel"

Her name was Lo - la;___ she was a show - girl___ with yel - low
Ri - co;___ he wore a dia - mond,___ He was es -
Lo - la;___ she was a show - girl, But that was

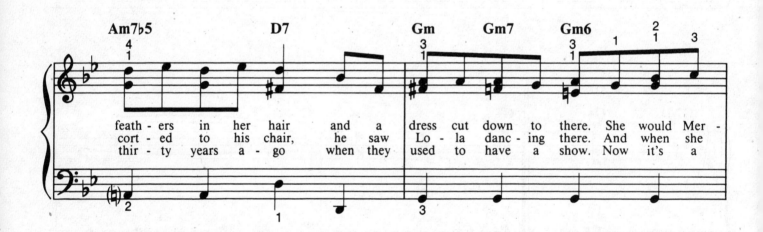

feath - ers in her hair and a dress cut down to there. She would Mer -
cort - ed to his chair, he saw Lo - la danc - ing there. And when she
thir - ty years a - go when they used to have a show. Now it's a

en - gue___ and do the Cha - Cha, And while she
fin - ished,___ he called her o - ver.___ But Ri - co
Dis - co,___ but not for Lo - la.___ Still in the

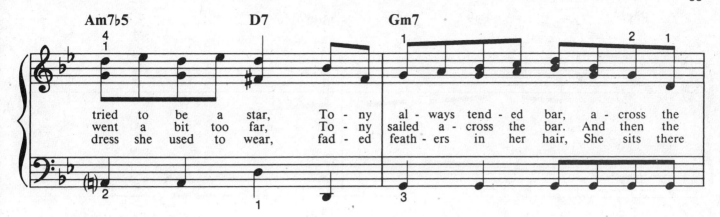

tried to be a star, To - ny al - ways tend - ed bar, a - cross the
went a bit too far, To - ny sailed a - cross the bar. And then the
dress she used to wear, fad - ed feath - ers in her hair, She sits there

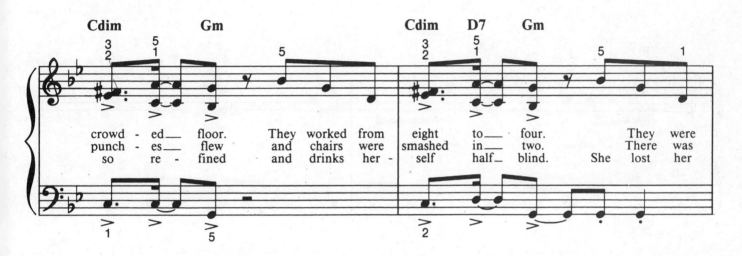

crowd - ed___ floor. They worked from eight to___ four. They were
punch - es___ flew and chairs were smashed in___ two. There was
so re - fined and drinks her - self half___ blind. She lost her

young and they had each oth - er, who could ask for more?⎫
blood and a sin - gle gun-shot, but just who shot who? ⎬ At the
youth and she lost her To - ny, now just she's lost her mind!⎭

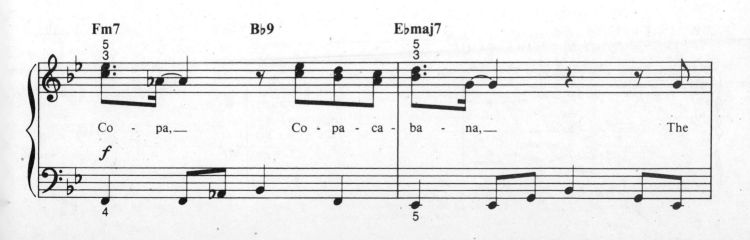

Co - pa,___ Co - pa - ca - ba - na,___ The

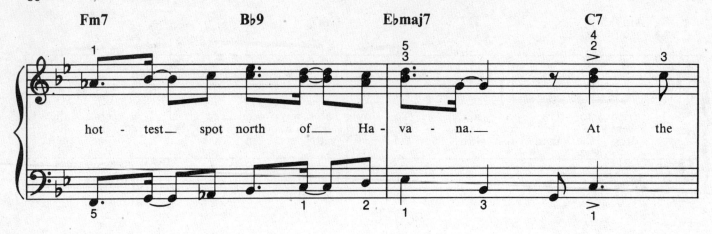

hot - test spot north of Ha - va - na. At the

Co - pa, Co - pa - ca - ba - na,

mu - sic and pas - sion were al - ways the fash - ion, At the

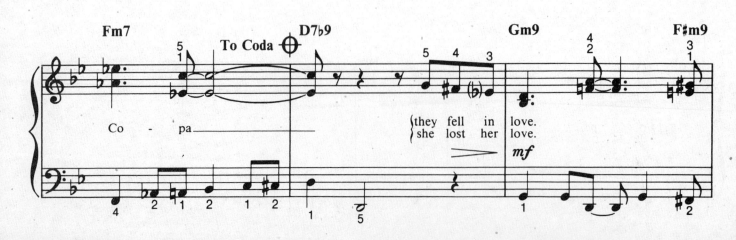

Co - pa

they fell in love.
she lost her love.

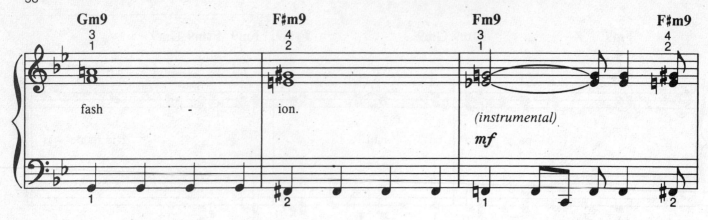

fash - ion. *(instrumental)* *mf*

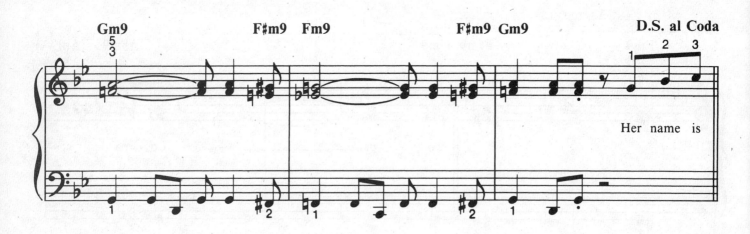

Her name is

CODA

don't fall in love, *mf* don't fall in

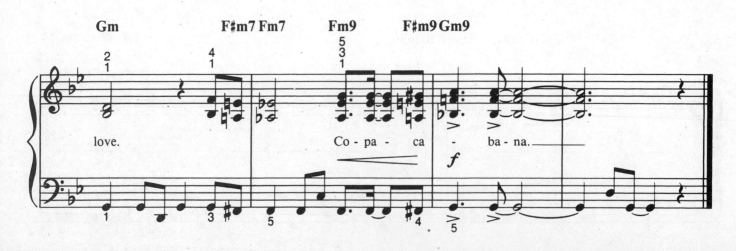

love. Co - pa - ca - ba - na. *f*

GETTING TO KNOW YOU

from THE KING AND I

Lyrics by OSCAR HAMMERSTEIN II
Music by RICHARD RODGERS

You are pre - cise - ly My cup of

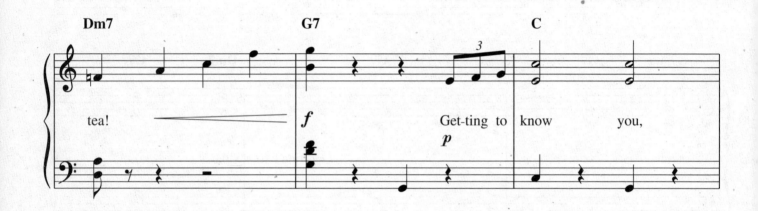

tea! Get-ting to know you,

get-ting to feel free and eas - y When I am

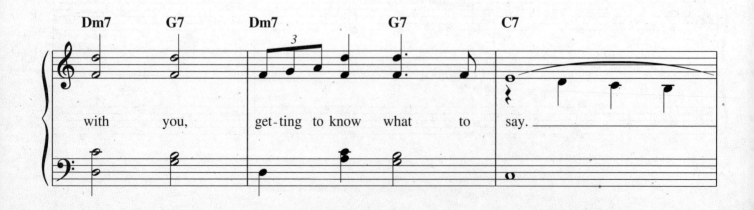

with you, get-ting to know what to say.

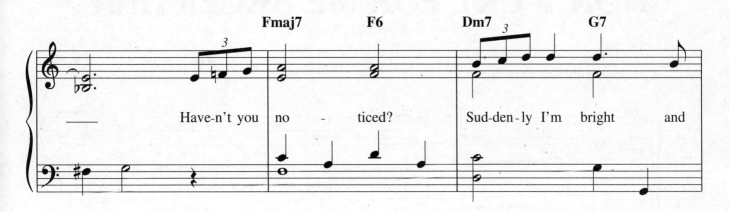

Have-n't you no - ticed? Sud-den-ly I'm bright and

breez - y, Be - cause of all the

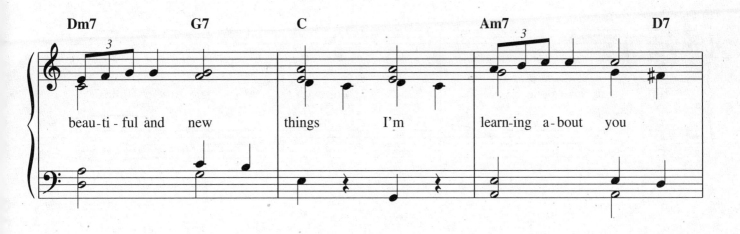

beau-ti-ful and new things I'm learn-ing a-bout you

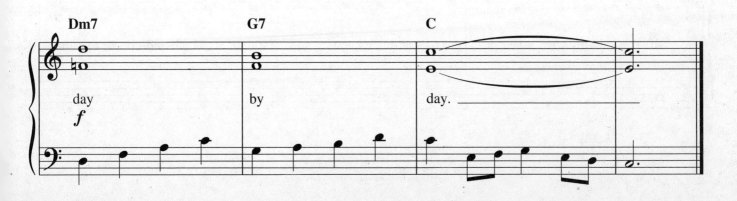

day by day.

DON'T CRY FOR ME ARGENTINA

from EVITA

Words by TIM RICE
Music by ANDREW LLOYD WEBBER

Moderate Tango tempo

It won't be eas-y, you'll think it strange when I

try to ex-plain how I feel, that I still need your love af-ter

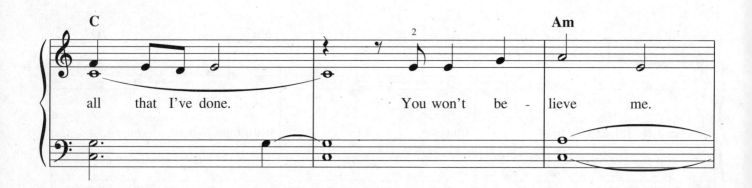

all that I've done. You won't be-lieve me.

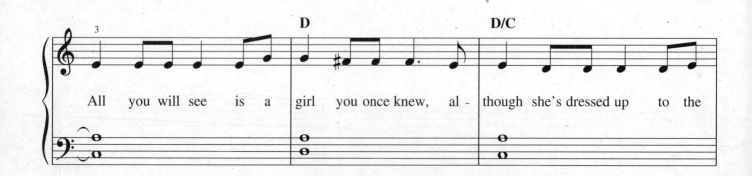

All you will see is a girl you once knew, al-though she's dressed up to the

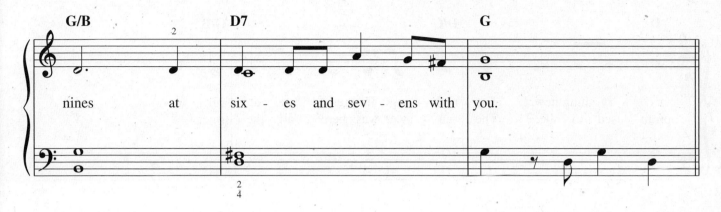

nines   at   six - es and sev - ens with   you.

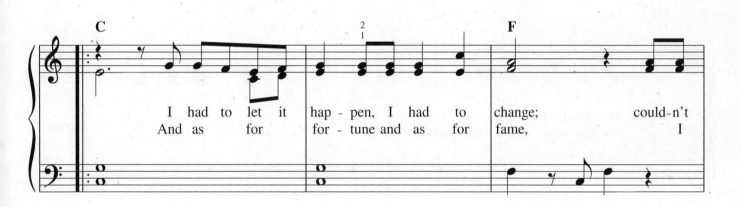

I   had   to   let   it   hap - pen, I had   to   change;   could-n't
And   as   for   for - tune and as   for   fame,   I

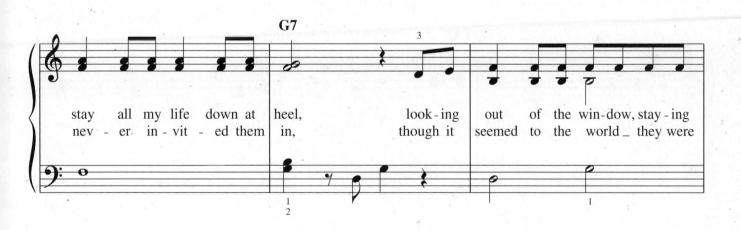

stay   all my life down at   heel,   look-ing   out   of the win-dow, stay-ing
nev - er in-vit-ed them   in,   though it   seemed to the world_ they were

out   of the sun,   So   I chose free - dom,   run - ning a-round try - ing
all   I de-sired.   They are   il - lu - sions, they're not   the so - lu - tions they

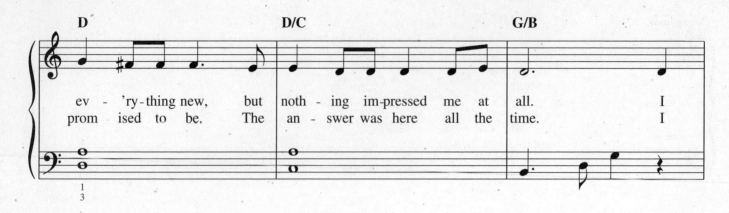

ev - 'ry-thing new, but noth - ing im-pressed me at all. I
prom ised to be. The an - swer was here all the time. I

nev - er ex - pect - ed it to.
love you and hope you love me,

Don't cry for me Ar - gen -

ti - na, ___ the truth is I nev - er left you. All through my

To Coda

wild days, my mad ex - ist-ence, I kept my prom-ise. Don't keep your

dis - tance.

Have I said too much? There's

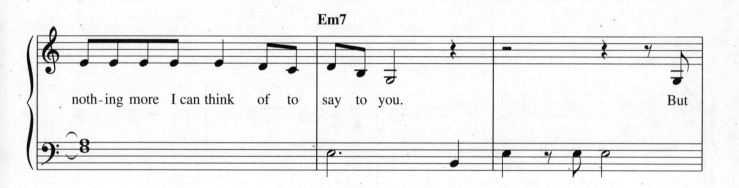

noth-ing more I can think of to say to you.

But

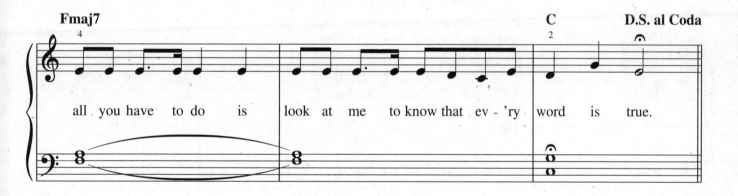

Fmaj7

C

D.S. al Coda

all you have to do is look at me to know that ev - 'ry word is true.

CODA

F

C

dis - tance.

FALLING IN LOVE WITH LOVE

from THE BOYS FROM SYRACUSE

Words by LORENZ HART
Music by RICHARD RODGERS

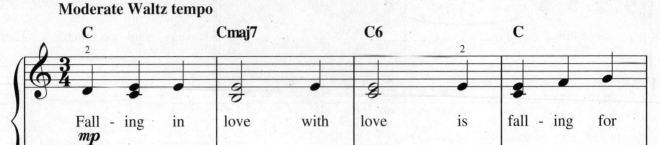

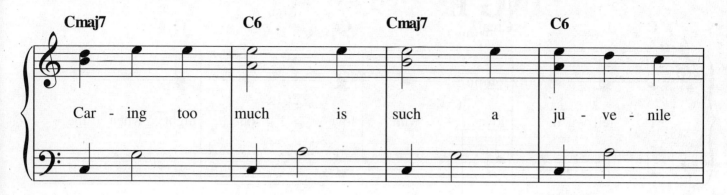

Cmaj7   C6   Cmaj7   C6

Car - ing too much is such a ju - ve - nile

E7sus   E7   G6   E7

fan - cy.

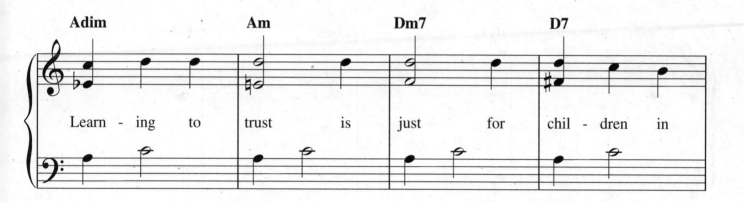

Adim   Am   Dm7   D7

Learn - ing to trust is just for chil - dren in

Dm7   G7

school.

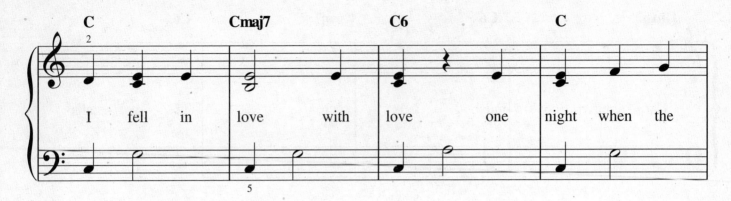

C   Cmaj7   C6   C

I fell in love with love one night when the

G7sus   G7   Dm7   G7

moon was full.

G7sus   G7   G7sus   G7

I was un - wise with eyes un - a - ble to

Cmaj7   C6   Cmaj7   C6

see.

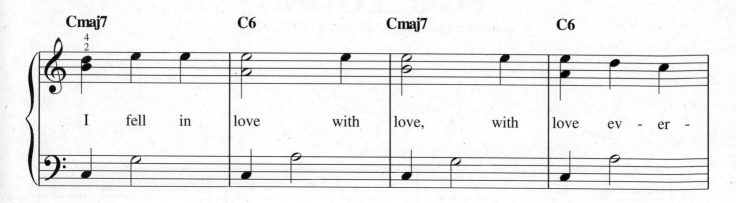

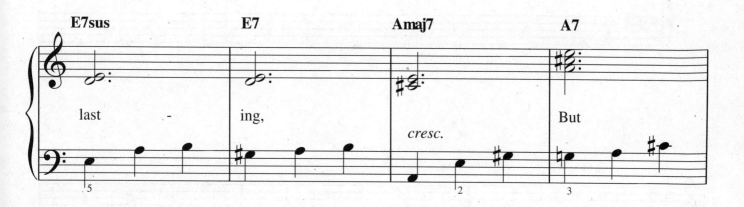

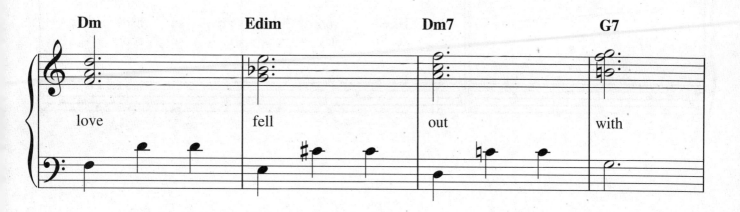

FOOTLOOSE

from the Broadway Musical FOOTLOOSE

Words by DEAN PITCHFORD and KENNY LOGGINS
Music by KENNY LOGGINS

I been work-in' so hard.
You're play-in' so cool,

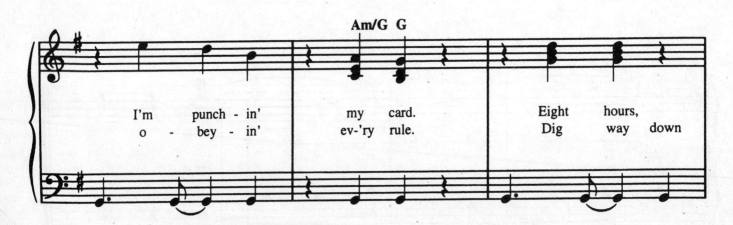

I'm punch-in' my card.
o-bey-in' ev-'ry rule.

Eight hours,
Dig way down

GUS: THE THEATRE CAT
from CATS

Music by ANDREW LLOYD WEBBER
Text by T.S. ELIOT

Moderately slow

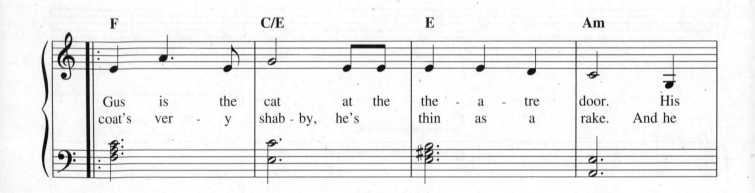

Gus is the cat at the the - a - tre door. His
coat's ver - y shab - by, he's thin as a rake. And he

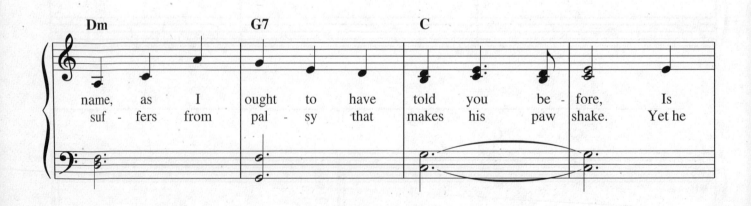

name, as I ought to have told you be - fore, Is
suf - fers from pal - sy that makes his paw shake. Yet he

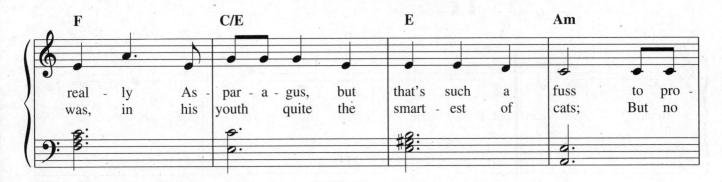

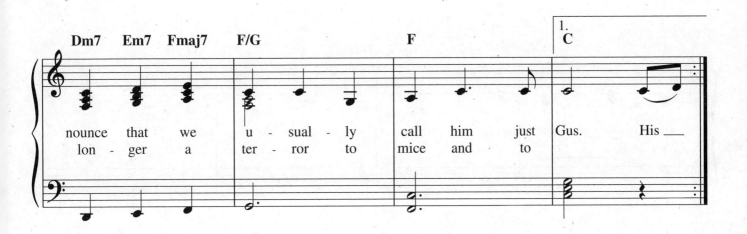

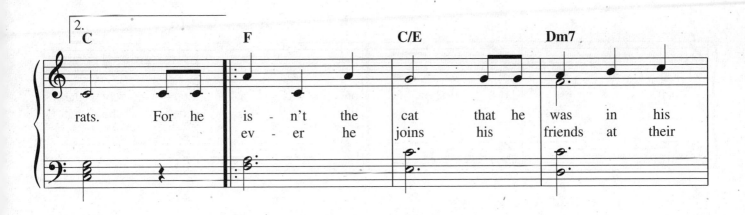

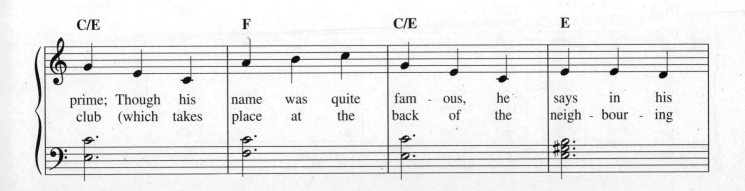

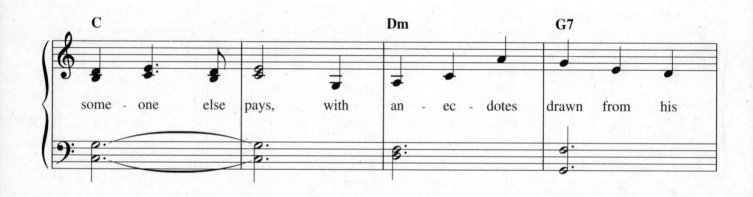

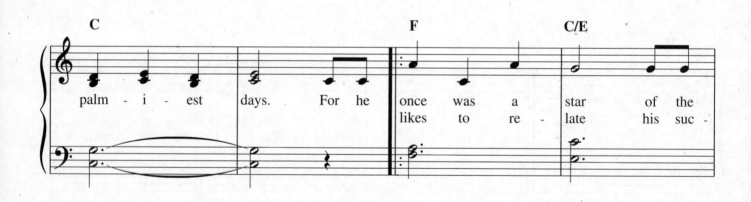

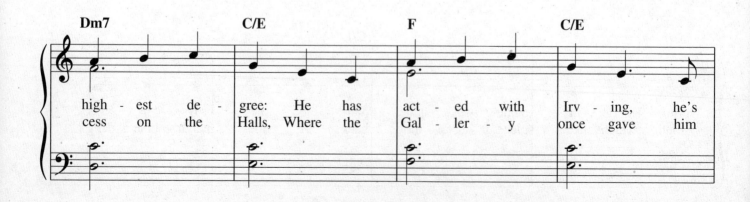

act - ed with Tree. And he
sev - en cat - calls. But his great - est cre - a - tion as

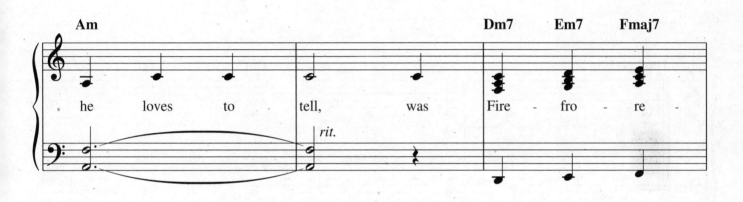

he loves to tell, was Fire - fro - re -

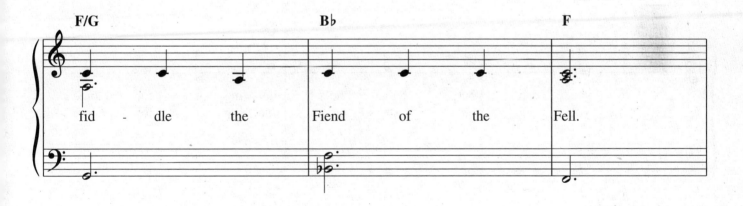

fid - dle the Fiend of the Fell.

GUYS AND DOLLS

from GUYS AND DOLLS

By FRANK LOESSER

John wait - ing out in the rain _____ chan - ces
doll with her dia - mond in hock, _____ rest as -

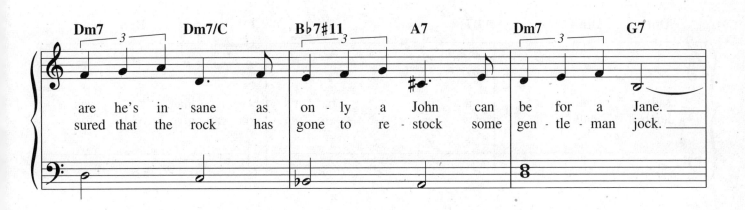

are he's in - sane as on - ly a John can be for a Jane. _____
sured that the rock has gone to re - stock some gen - tle - man jock. _____

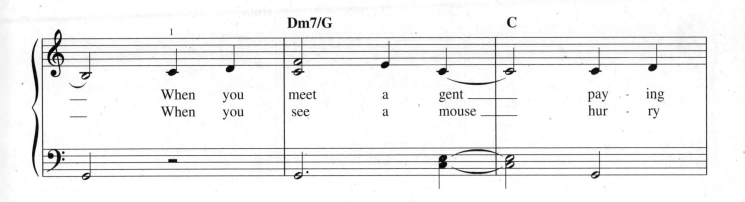

When you meet a gent _____ pay - ing
When you see a mouse _____ hur - ry

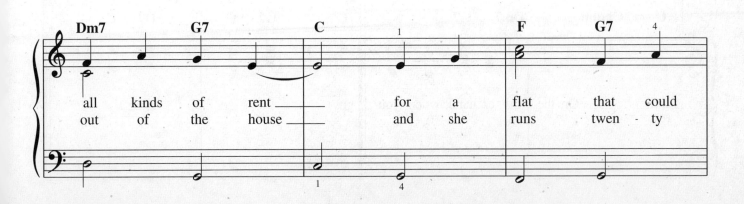

all kinds of rent _____ for a flat that could
out of the house _____ and she runs twen - ty

flat - ten the Taj Ma - hal, _____ call it
blocks for ci - gars and rye, _____ call it

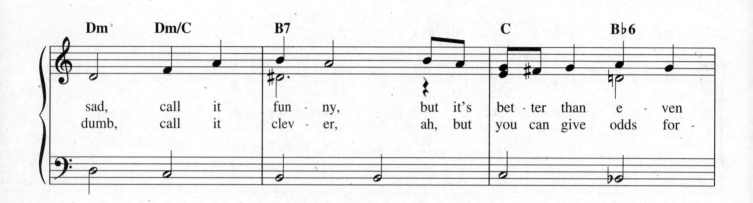

sad, call it fun - ny, but it's bet - ter than e - ven
dumb, call it clev - er, ah, but you can give odds for -

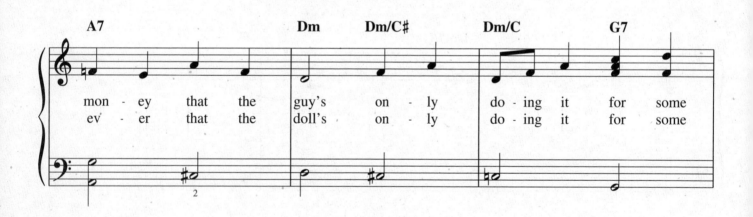

mon - ey that the guy's on - ly do - ing it for some
ev - er that the doll's on - ly do - ing it for some

doll. On the oth - er hand: when you guy.

I DREAMED A DREAM
from LES MISÉRABLES

Music by CLAUDE-MICHEL SCHÖNBERG
Lyrics by ALAIN BOUBLIL,
JEAN-MARC NATEL and HERBERT KRETZMER

I AIN'T DOWN YET
from THE UNSINKABLE MOLLY BROWN

By MEREDITH WILLSON

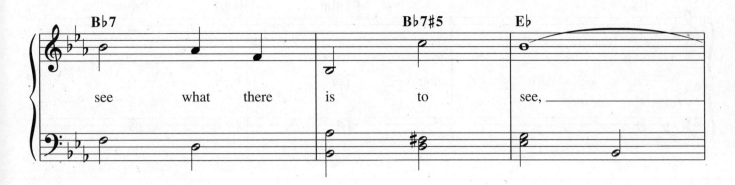

see   what   there   is   to   see, _____

____ So   if   you   go   from   no - where   on   the

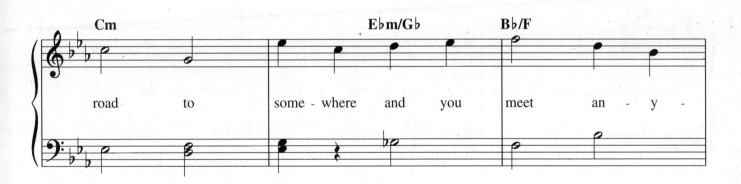

road   to   some - where   and   you   meet   an - y -

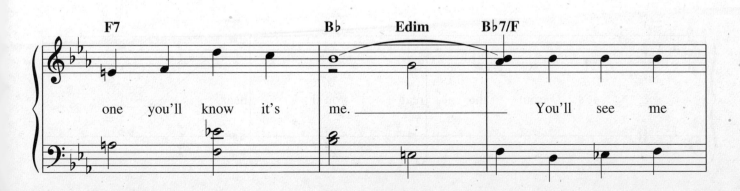

one   you'll   know   it's   me. _____   You'll   see   me

car - ried shoul - der high,

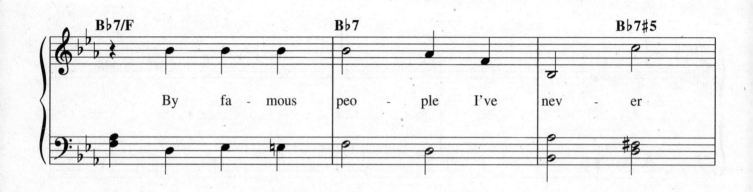

By fa - mous peo - ple I've nev - er

met, _____ but till I leave the rear,

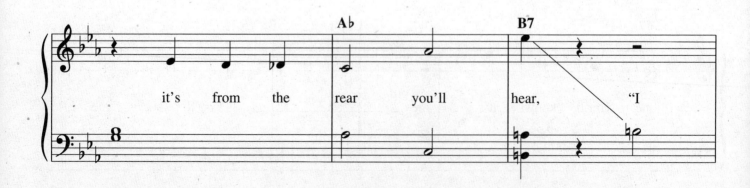

it's from the rear you'll hear, "I

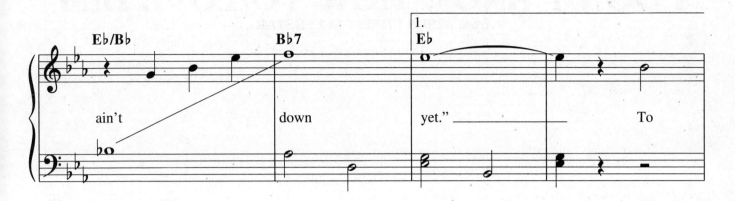

ain't   down   yet." _____   To

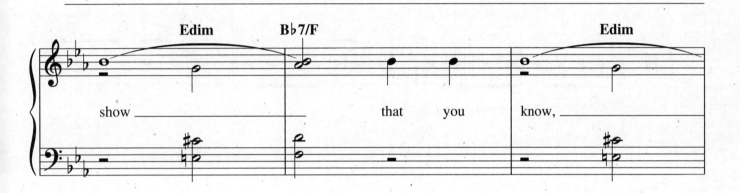

show _____   that   you   know, _____

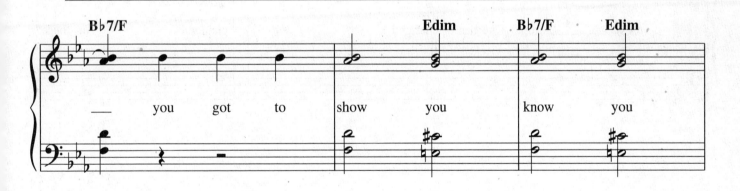

__   you   got   to   show   you   know   you

know!   I'm   goan'   to   yet." _____

I DON'T KNOW HOW TO LOVE HIM
from JESUS CHRIST SUPERSTAR

Words by TIM RICE
Music by ANDREW LLOYD WEBBER

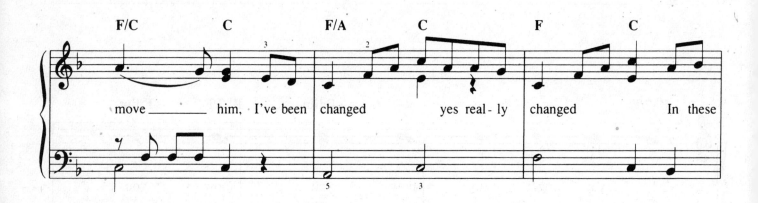

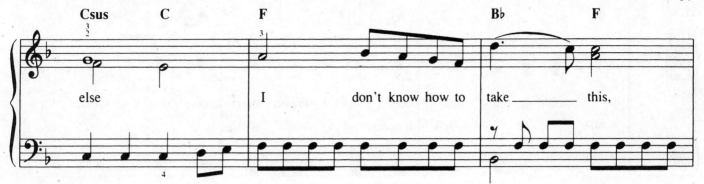

else I don't know how to take _____ this,

I don't see why he moves _____ me, He's a man he's just a

man And I've had so ma-ny men be-fore in

ve-ry ma-ny ways He's just one more.

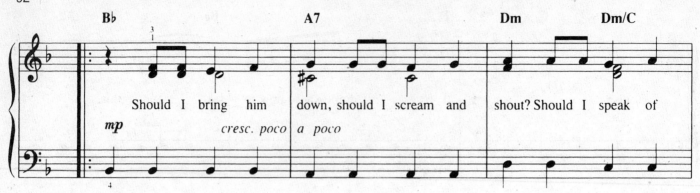

Should I bring him down, should I scream and shout? Should I speak of

love let my feel-ings out? I nev-er thought I'd come to this

what's it all a-bout?

Don't you think it's rath-er fun — ny I should be in this po-
Yet if he said he loved _____ me I'd be lost I'd be

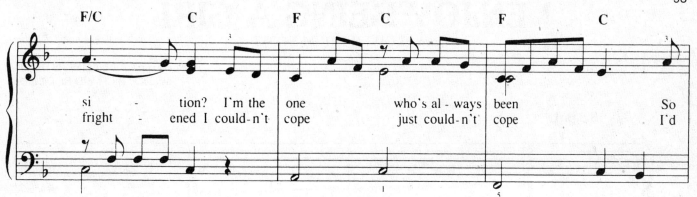

si - tion? I'm the one who's al - ways been So
fright - ened I could-n't cope just could-n't cope I'd

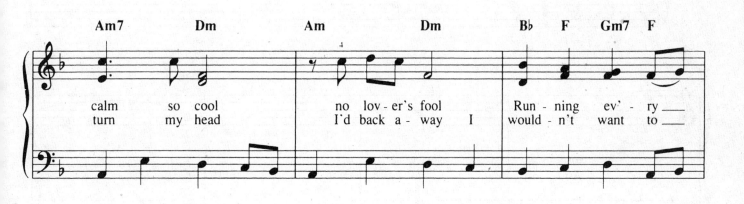

calm so cool no lov-er's fool Run - ning ev' - ry___
turn my head I'd back a - way I would-n't want to___

show He scares me so
know He scares me so I want him

so I love him so.

rit.

I ENJOY BEING A GIRL
from FLOWER DRUM SONG

Lyrics by OSCAR HAMMERSTEIN II
Music by RICHARD RODGERS

girl!
girl!
When

flip when a fel - low sends me flow - ers,

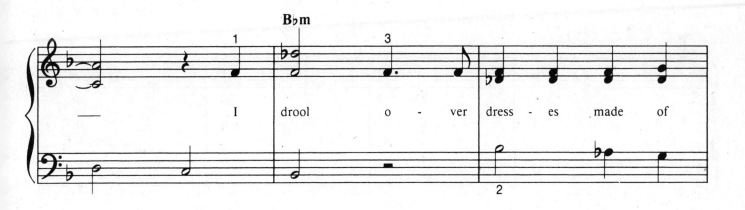

I drool o - ver dress - es made of

lace. I talk on the tel - e - phone for

ho - urs ___ With a pound and a half of

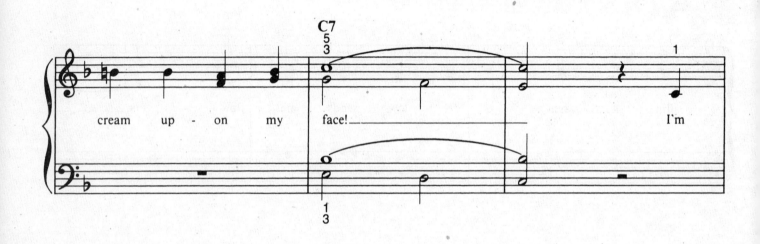

cream up - on my face! ___ I'm

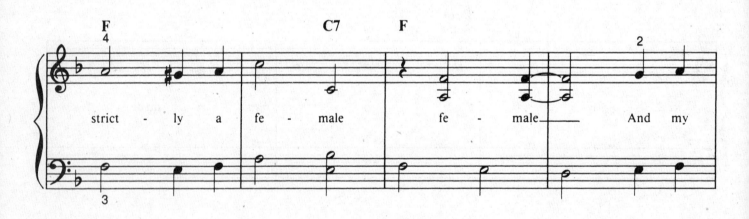

strict - ly a fe - male fe - male ___ And my

fu - ture I hope will be ___ In the

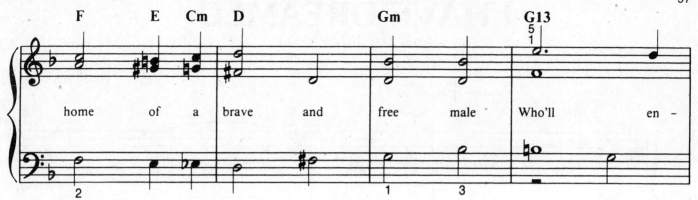

home   of   a   brave   and   free   male   Who'll   en -

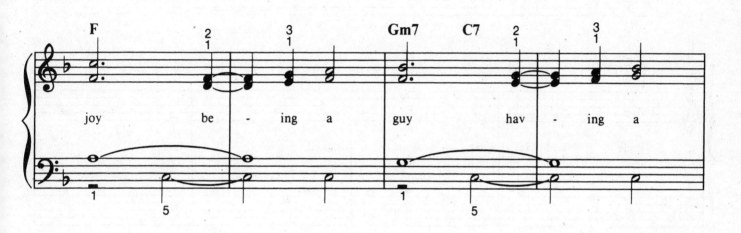

joy   be - ing   a   guy   hav - ing   a

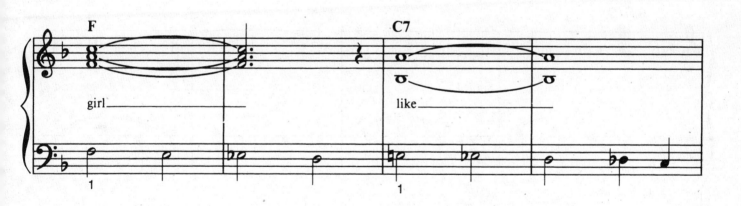

girl _____   like _____

me.

I HAVE DREAMED

from THE KING AND I

Lyrics by OSCAR HAMMERSTEIN II
Music by RICHARD RODGERS

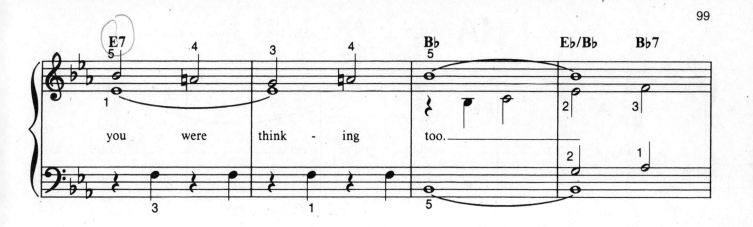

you were think - ing too.

Slowly, very smoothly

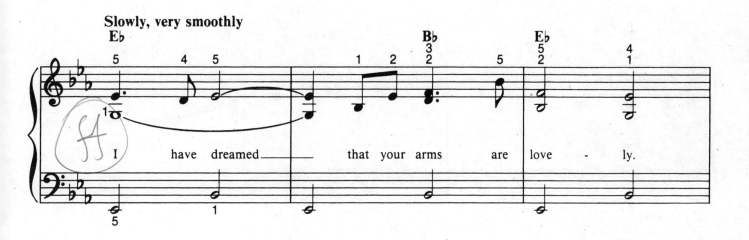

I have dreamed that your arms are love - ly.

I have dreamed what a joy you'll

be. I have dreamed ev - 'ry word you'll

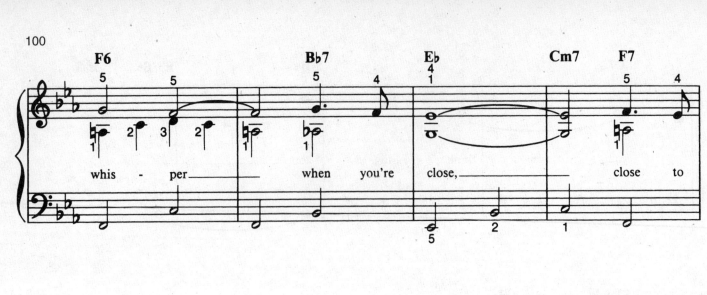

whis - per___ when you're close,_____ close to

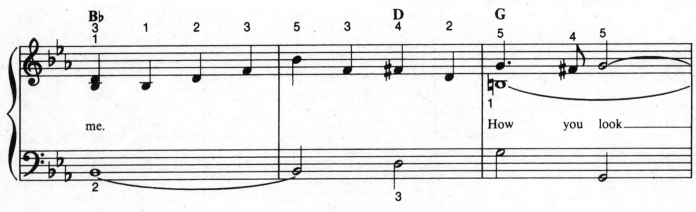

me. How you look___

___ in the glow of eve - ning,

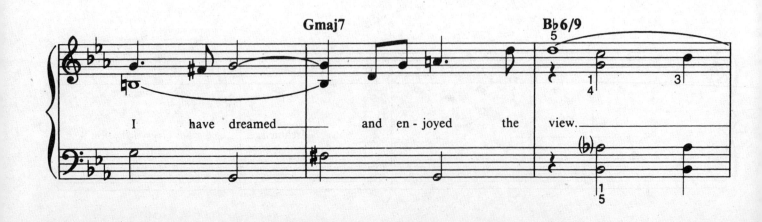

I have dreamed___ and en - joyed the view.___

In these dreams I've loved you so. that by

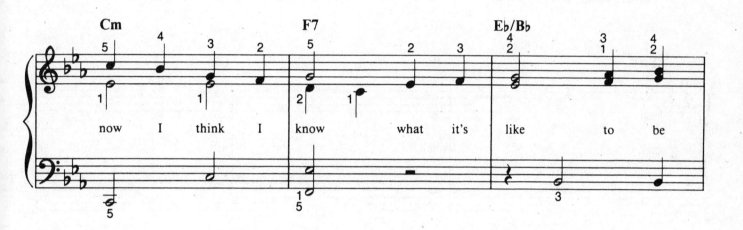

now I think I know what it's like to be

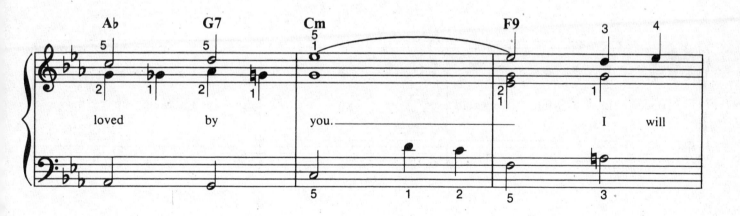

loved by you. I will

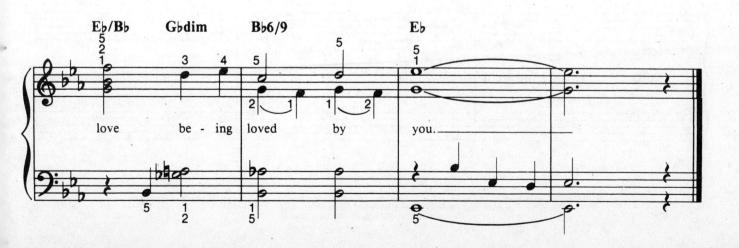

love be - ing loved by you.

I WILL NEVER LEAVE YOU
from SIDE SHOW

Words by BILL RUSSELL
Music by HENRY KRIEGER

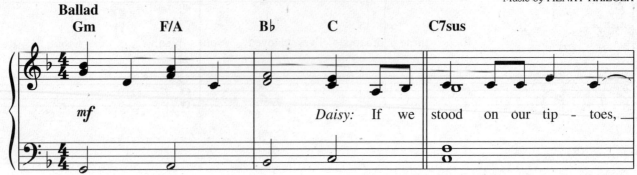

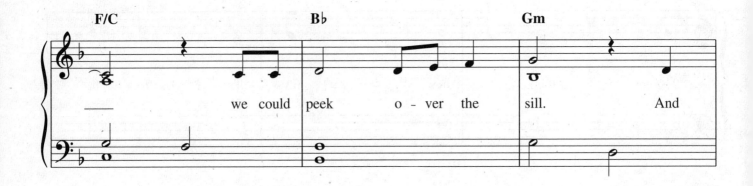

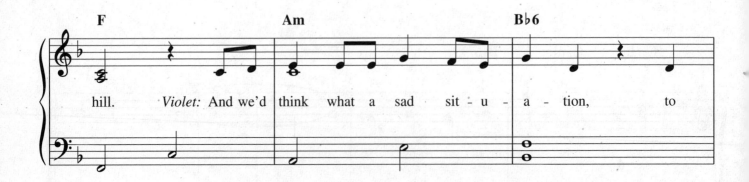

be out-side __ on your own, *Daisy:* to go through the town with no

play-mate, *Violet:* to go through life all a-lone. *Both:* I will nev-er

leave you. I will nev-er go a-way. __

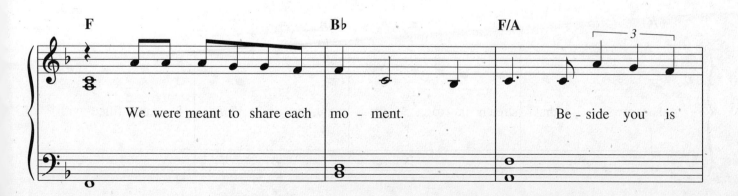

We were meant to share each mo-ment. Be-side you is

where I will stay. Ev - er - more and

al - ways, we'll be one tho' we're two. For I will

nev - er leave you. *Daisy:* When the day is filled with

shad - ows that stretch in - to __ the night, *Violet:* I am filled with

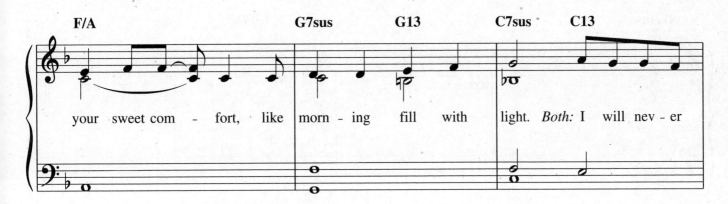

F/A   G7sus   G13   C7sus   C13

your sweet com - fort, like morn - ing fill with light. *Both:* I will nev - er

F   Eb/F

leave you,   I will nev - er go a - way. __

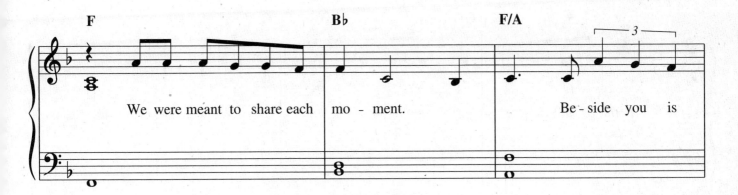

F   Bb   F/A

We were meant to share each mo - ment.   Be - side you is

Gm   A   Dm   Dm/C

where I will stay.   Ev - er - more and al - ways, we'll be

one tho' we're two. For I will nev - er

leave you. *Daisy:* I will nev - er leave you.

Both: I will nev - er go a - way. ___ We were meant to share each

mo - ment. *Daisy:* Be - side you is where I will stay.

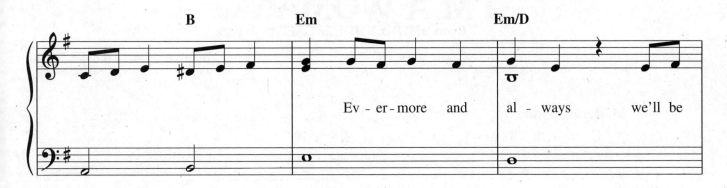

Ev - er - more and al - ways we'll be

one tho' we're two. For I will

nev - er, I will nev - er,

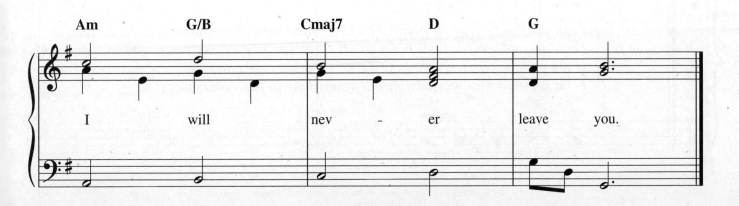

I will nev - er leave you.

I'M A WOMAN

from SMOKEY JOE'S CAFE

Words and Music by JERRY LEIBER
and MIKE STOLLER

Moderate Swing

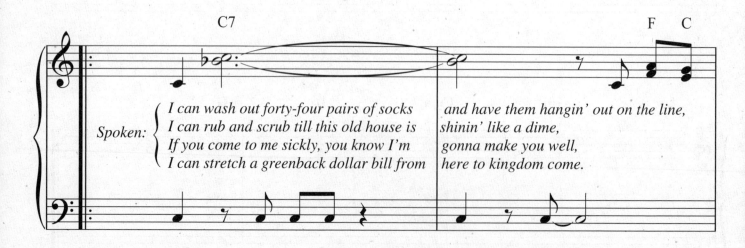

Spoken:

I can wash out forty-four pairs of socks
I can rub and scrub till this old house is
If you come to me sickly, you know I'm
I can stretch a greenback dollar bill from

and have them hangin' out on the line,
shinin' like a dime,
gonna make you well,
here to kingdom come.

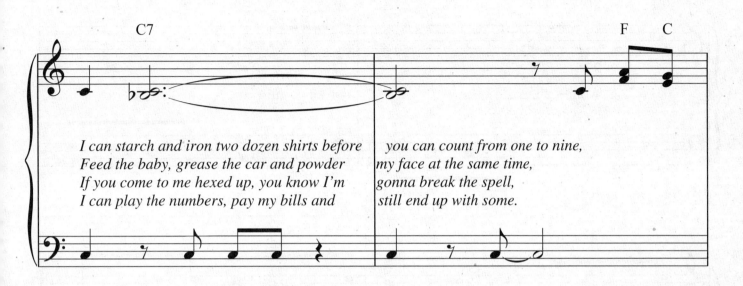

C7   **F**   **C**

I can starch and iron two dozen shirts before   *you can count from one to nine,*
Feed the baby, grease the car and powder   *my face at the same time,*
If you come to me hexed up, you know I'm   *gonna break the spell,*
I can play the numbers, pay my bills and   *still end up with some.*

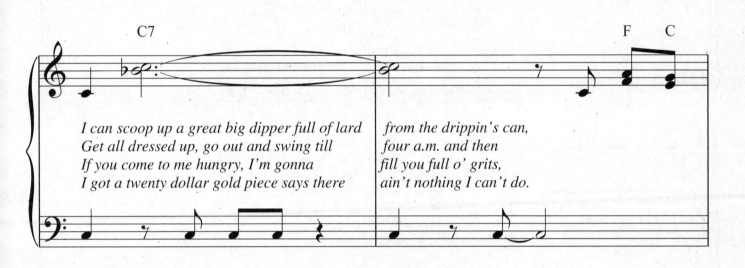

C7   **F**   **C**

I can scoop up a great big dipper full of lard   *from the drippin's can,*
Get all dressed up, go out and swing till   *four a.m. and then*
If you come to me hungry, I'm gonna   *fill you full o' grits,*
I got a twenty dollar gold piece says there   *ain't nothing I can't do.*

C7

'Cause I'm a

Throw it in the skillet, go out and do my shopping   *and be back before it melts in the pan,*
Lay down at five, jump up at six and   *start all over again,*
If it's love you're lackin', I'll kiss you and   *give you the shiverin' fits,*
I can make a dress out of a feedbag and I can   *make a man out of you,*

IF I WERE A BELL
from GUYS AND DOLLS

By FRANK LOESSER

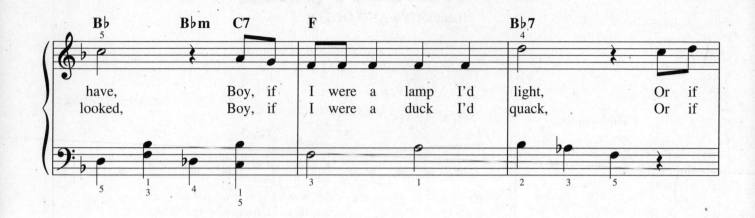

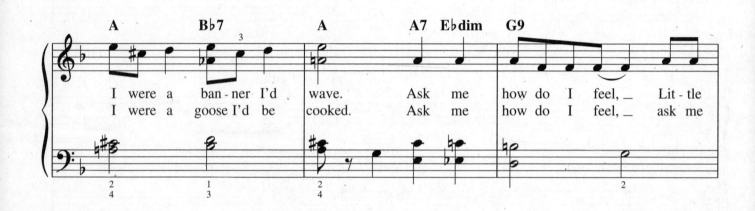

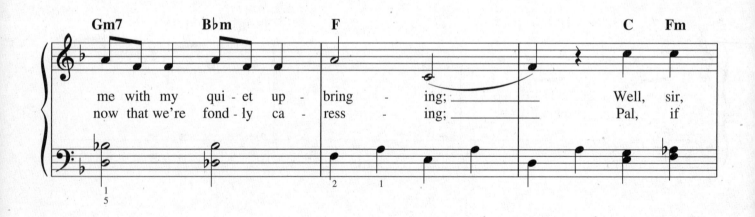

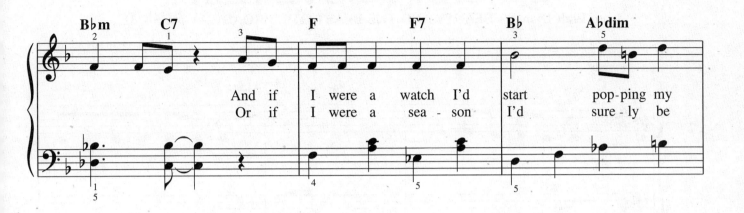

And if I were a watch I'd start pop-ping my
Or if I were a sea - son I'd sure-ly be

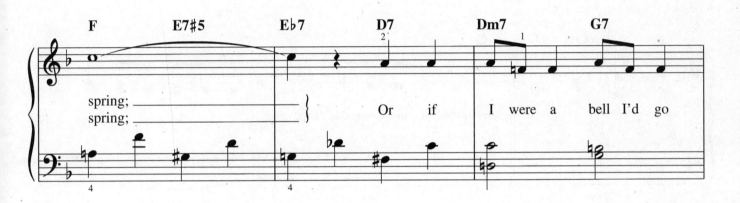

spring; _____
spring; _____
Or if I were a bell I'd go

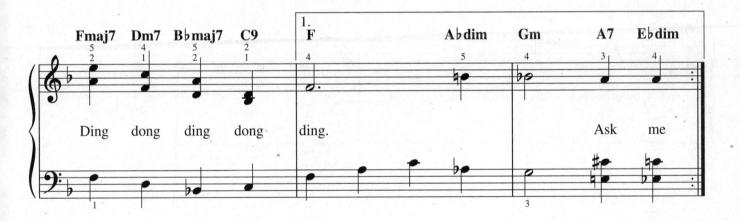

Ding dong ding dong ding.
Ask me

ding.

IF I CAN'T LOVE HER

from Walt Disney's BEAUTY AND THE BEAST: THE BROADWAY MUSICAL

Music by ALAN MENKEN
Lyrics by TIM RICE

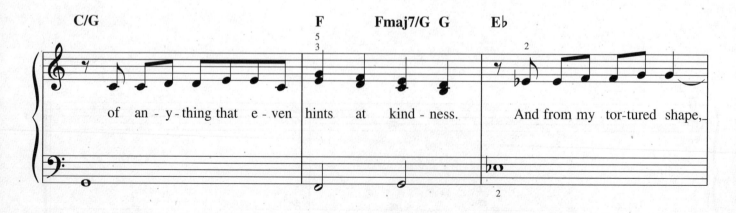

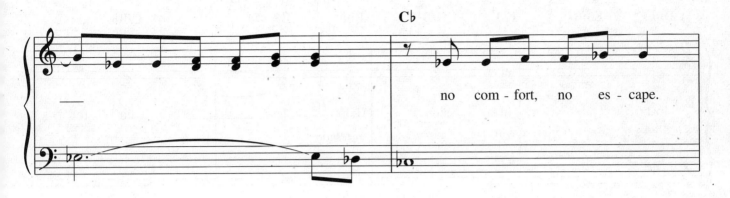

no com - fort, no es - cape.

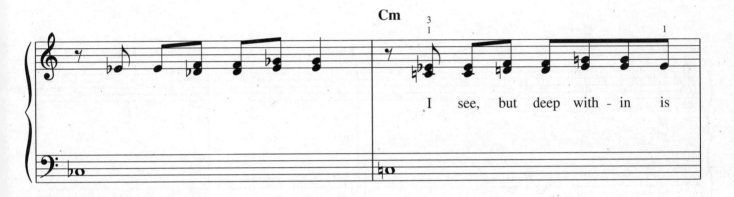

I see, but deep with - in is

With more motion

Fm   Gsus   G7   Em   B♭   C/B♭

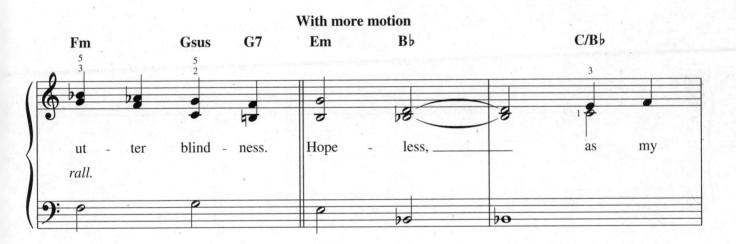

ut - ter blind - ness.   Hope - less, _____   as my

rall.

F/A   C/G   F6/9   C/E

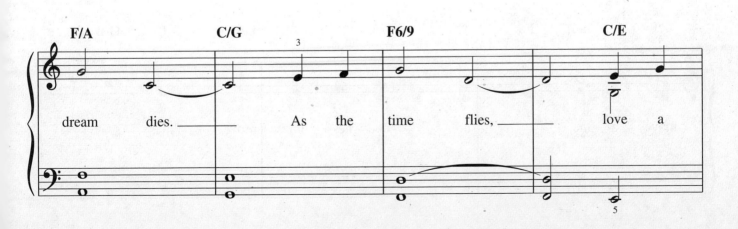

dream dies. _____   As the time flies, _____   love a

116

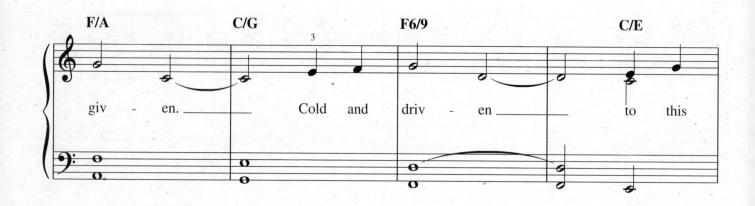

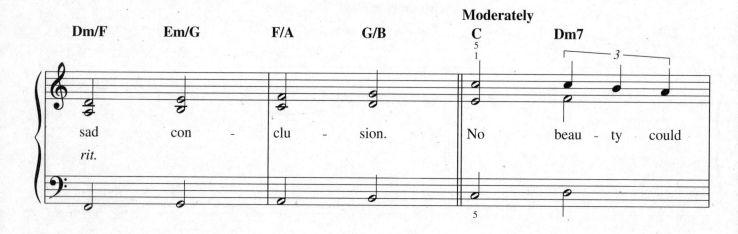

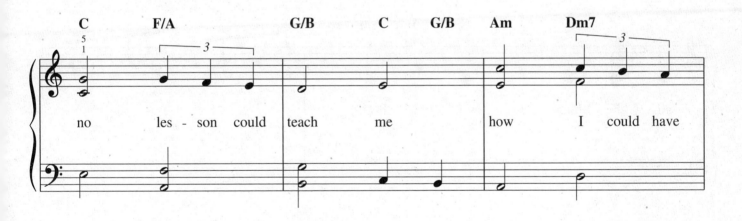

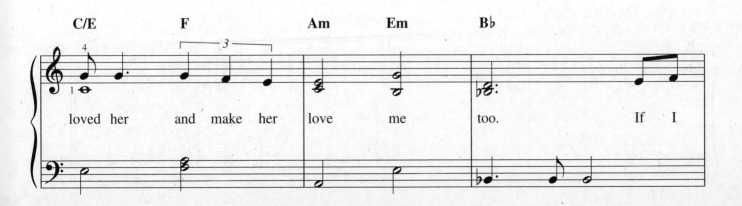

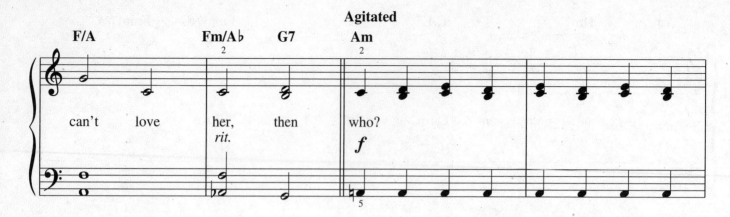

can't love her, then who?

rit.

Long a - go, I should have seen

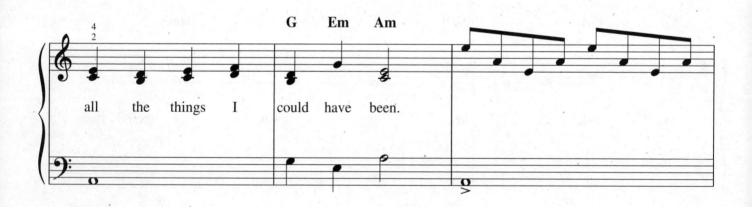

all the things I could have been.

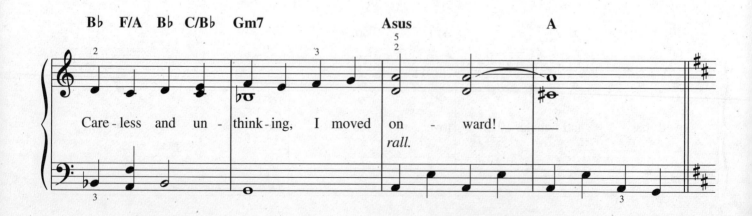

Care - less and un - think - ing, I moved on - ward!

rall.

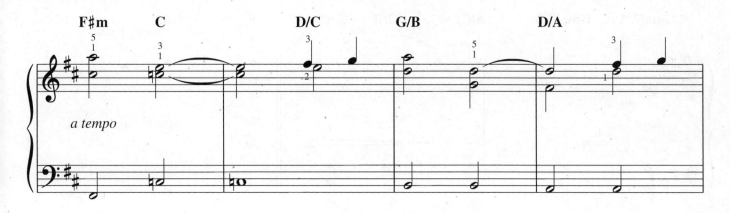

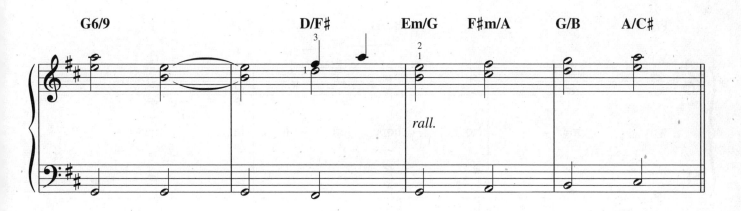

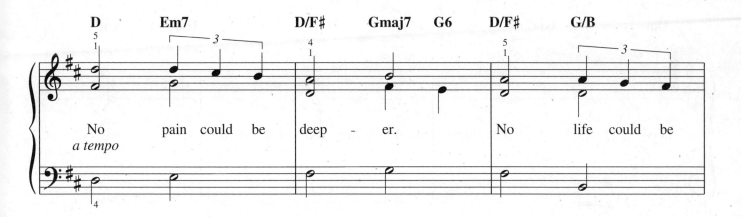

No pain could be deep - er. No life could be

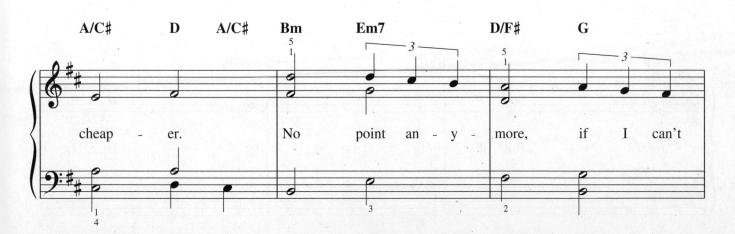

cheap - er. No point an - y - more, if I can't

Gmaj7/A   Gmaj7/B   A/C♯   G/B   A/C♯   F   Gm7

love   her.   No   spir - it could

F/A   B♭   F/C   B♭/D   C/E   F   C/E

win   me.   No   hope   left   with - in   me,

Dm   Gm7   F/A   B♭   Dm   Am

hope   I   could have   loved   her   and   that   she'd   set   me

E♭   B♭/D   B♭m6/D♭

free.   But   it's   not   to   be.   If   I

can't love her,

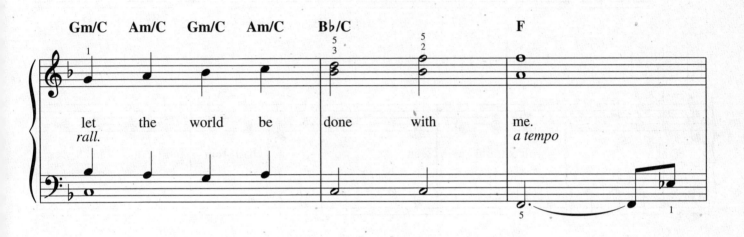

let the world be done with me.
rall.   *a tempo*

IF MY FRIENDS COULD SEE ME NOW
from SWEET CHARITY

Words by DOROTHY FIELDS
Music by CY COLEMAN

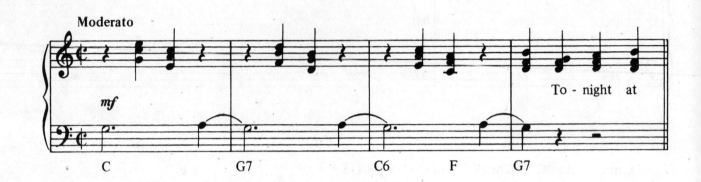

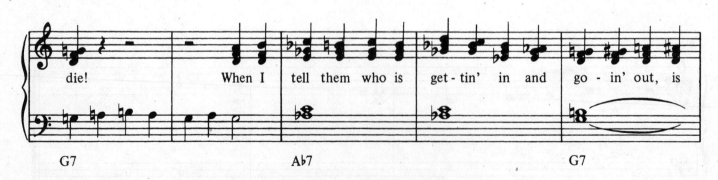

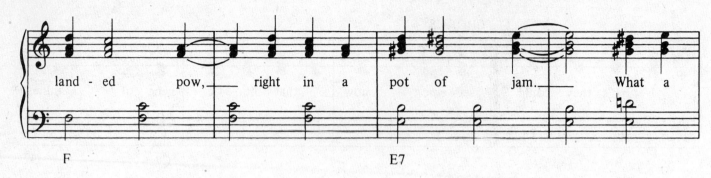

land - ed pow,___ right in a pot of jam.___ What a

F   E7

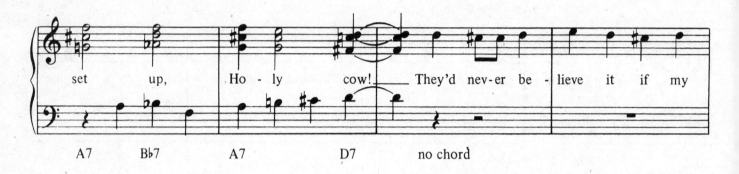

set up, Ho - ly cow!___ They'd nev-er be - lieve it if my

A7   Bb7   A7   D7   no chord

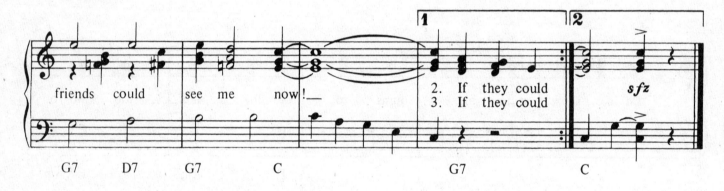

friends could see me now!___

2. If they could
3. If they could

sfz

G7   D7   G7   C   G7   C

2. If they could see me now,
   My little dusty group,
   Traipsin' round this million dollar chicken coop.
   I'd hear those thrift shop cats say: "Brother, get her!
   Draped on a bedspread made from three kinds of fur."
   All I can say is "Wow!
   Wait till the riff and raff
   See just exactly how he signed this autograph."
   What a build-up, Holy cow!
   They'd never believe it, if my friends could see me now.

3. If they could see me now,
   Alone with Mr V.,
   Who's waitin' on me like he was a maitre d'.
   I hear my buddies saying, "Crazy, what gives?
   Tonight she's living like the other half lives."
   To think the highest brow,
   Which I must say is he,
   Should pick the lowest brow, which there's no doubt is me.
   What a step up, Holy cow!
   They'd never believe it, if my friends could see me now.

LEANING ON A LAMP POST

from ME AND MY GIRL

By NOEL GAY

Lean - ing on a lamp, May - be you

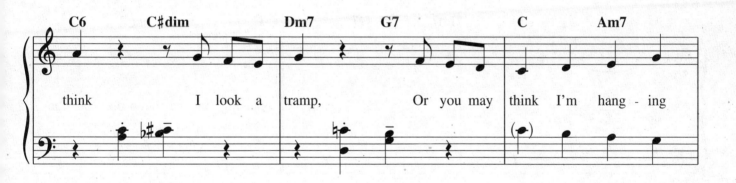

think I look a tramp, Or you may think I'm hang - ing

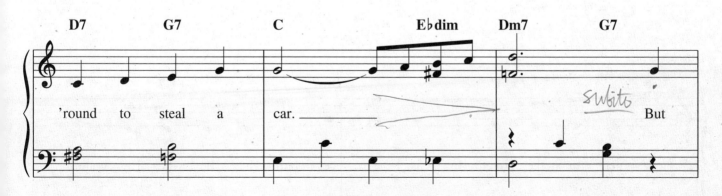

'round to steal a car. _____ But

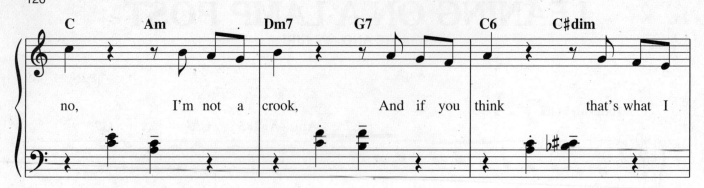

no, I'm not a crook, And if you think that's what I

look, I'll tell you why I'm here and what my mo - tives

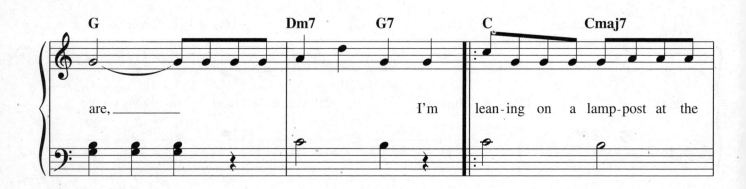

are, _____ I'm lean-ing on a lamp-post at the

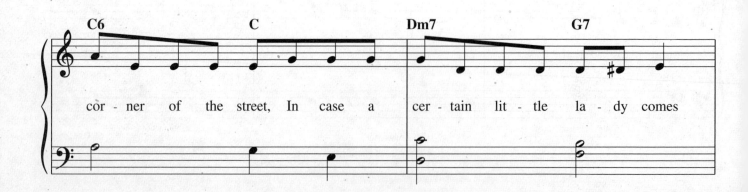

cor - ner of the street, In case a cer - tain lit - tle la - dy comes

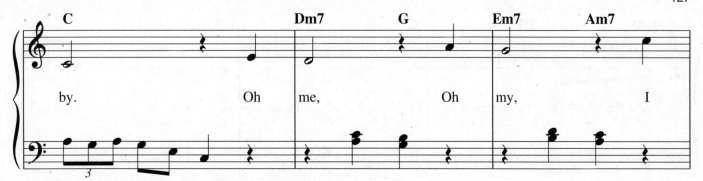

by.   Oh   me,   Oh   my,   I

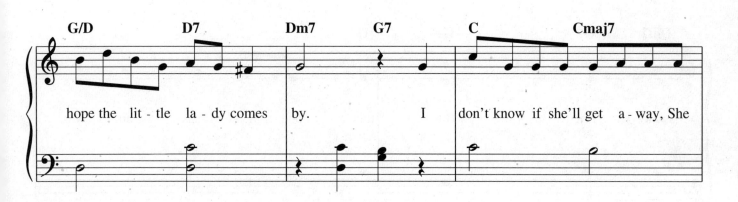

hope the lit - tle la - dy comes   by.   I   don't know if she'll get a - way, She

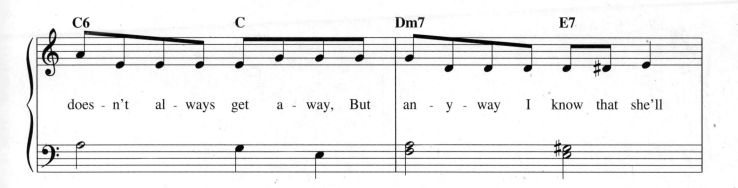

does - n't al - ways get a - way, But   an - y - way   I   know that she'll

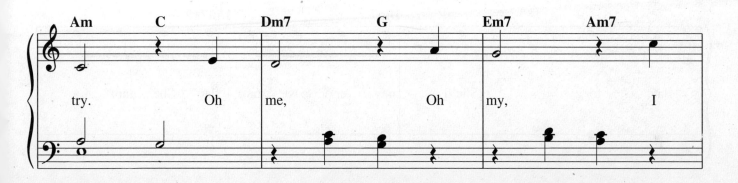

try.   Oh   me,   Oh   my,   I

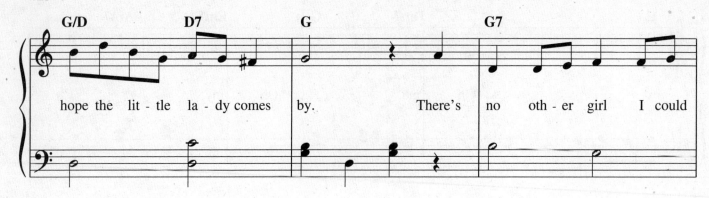

hope the lit - tle la - dy comes by. There's no oth - er girl I could

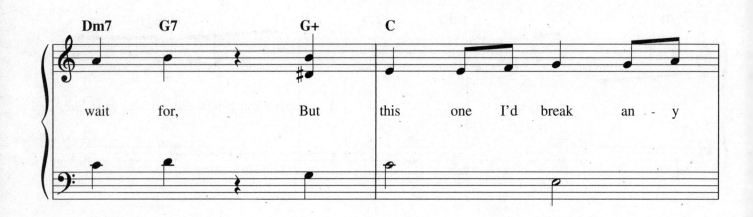

wait for, But this one I'd break an - y

date for, I won't have to ask what she's

late for, She'd nev - er leave me flat, She not a

girl like that. She's ab - so - lute - ly won - der - ful and

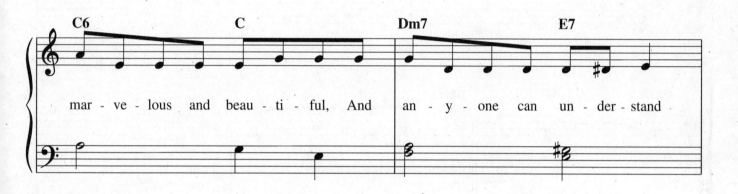

mar - ve - lous and beau - ti - ful, And an - y - one can un - der - stand

why I'm lean - ing on a lamp-post at the cor - ner of the street, In case a

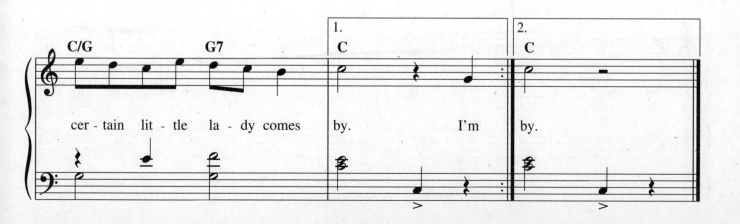

cer - tain lit - tle la - dy comes by. I'm by.

THE IMPOSSIBLE DREAM
(The Quest)
from MAN OF LA MANCHA

Lyric by JOE DARION
Music by MITCH LEIGH

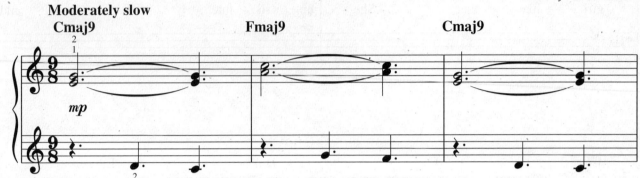

To dream ___ the im-pos-si-ble dream, _____ to

fight ___ the un-beat-a-ble foe, _____ to bear ___ the un-bear-a-ble

sor-row, _____ to run ___ where the brave dare not

go. _____ To right _____ the un-right-a-ble wrong, _____ to

love _____ pure and chaste from a - far, _____ to try _____ when your arms are too

wea-ry, _____ to reach _____ the un-reach-a-ble star! This is my

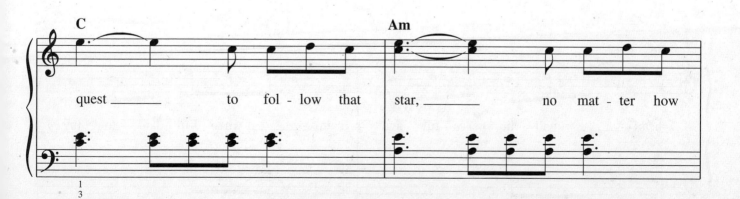

quest _____ to fol-low that star, _____ no mat-ter how

hope-less, ____ no mat-ter how far; ____ to fight for the right __ with-out ques-tion or

pause, __ to be will-ing to march in - to hell for a heav-en - ly cause! _____ And I

know _____ if I'll on - ly be true _____ to this glo - ri - ous quest _____ that my

heart _____ will lie peace - ful and calm _____ when I'm laid to my

rest. And the world __ will be bet-ter for this: _____ that one

man, __ scorned and cov-ered with scars, _____ still __ strove __ with his last ounce of

cour-age _____ to reach __ the un-reach-a - ble stars. _____

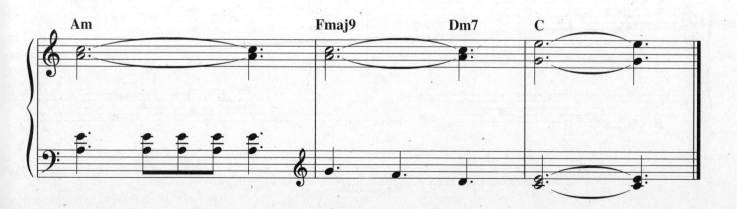

KANSAS CITY
from SMOKEY JOE'S CAFE

Words and Music by JERRY LEIBER
and MIKE STOLLER

C ... **G7**

come. They got a cra - zy way of lov - in' there and

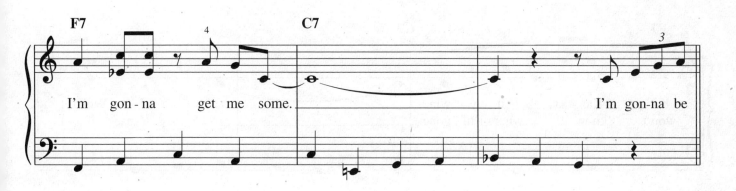

F7 ... **C7**

I'm gon - na get me some. _____ I'm gon-na be

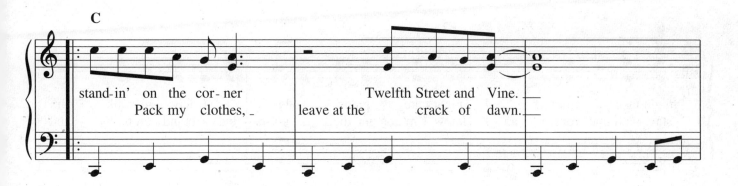

C

stand-in' on the cor - ner Twelfth Street and Vine.

Pack my clothes, _ leave at the crack of dawn. _

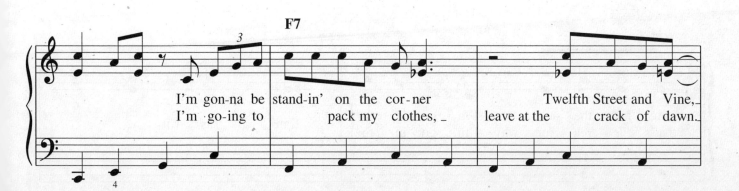

F7

I'm gon-na be stand-in' on the cor - ner Twelfth Street and Vine, _

I'm go-ing to pack my clothes, _ leave at the crack of dawn. _

with my Kan-sas Cit-y ba-by and a
My old la-dy will be sleep-in' an' she

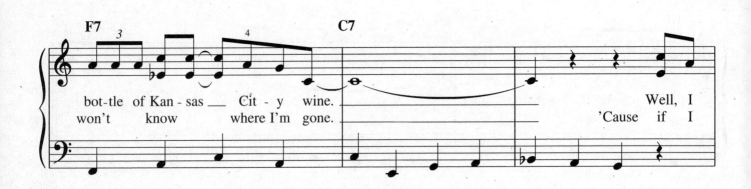

bot-tle of Kan-sas ___ Cit-y wine. _____ Well, I
won't know where I'm gone. _____ 'Cause if I

might take a train, _____ I might take a plane, _____ but if I have to walk I'm
stay with that wom - an I know I'm gon-na die, _____ got-ta find a brand new ba-by and

goin' just the same. I'm go-in' to Kan - sas Cit-y,
that's the rea-son why I'm go-in' to

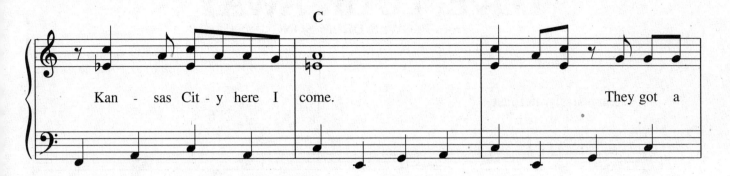

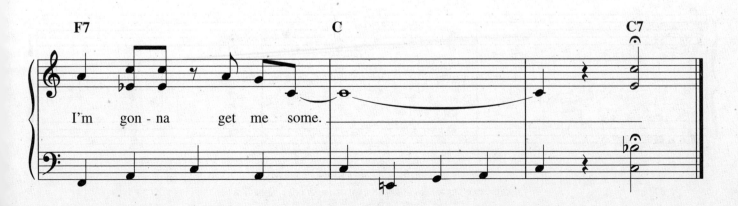

LOVE, LOOK AWAY
from FLOWER DRUM SONG

Lyrics by OSCAR HAMMERSTEIN II
Music by RICHARD RODGERS

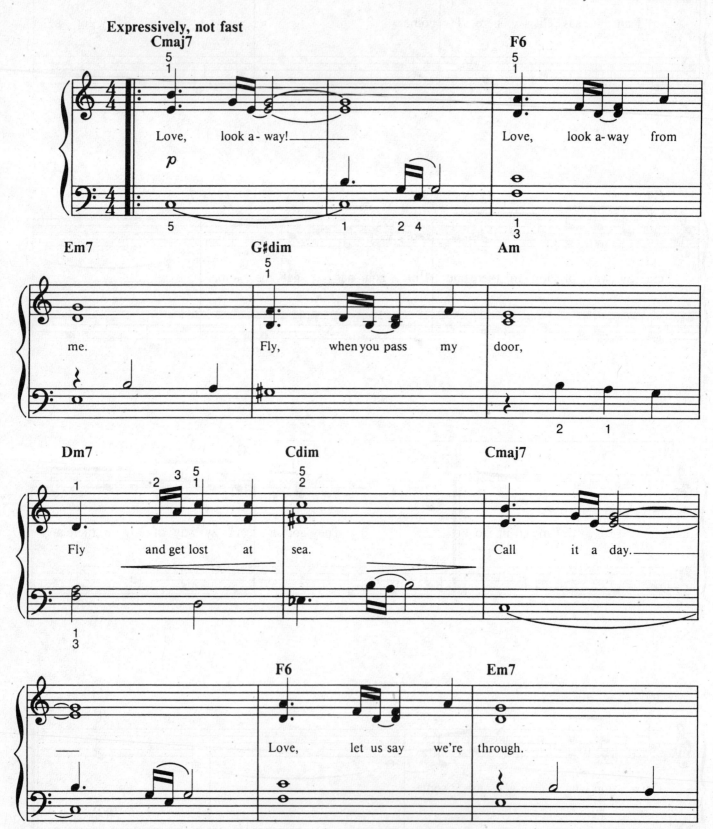

G#dim / Am / F6 / F6/G

No good are you for me, No good am I for

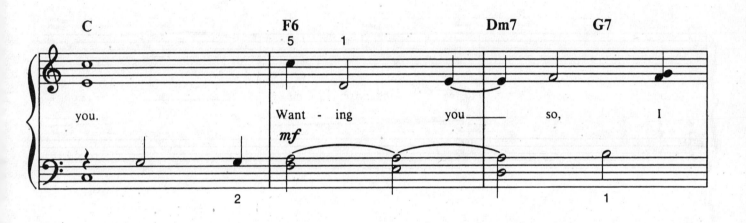

C / F6 / Dm7 / G7

you. Want - ing you so, I

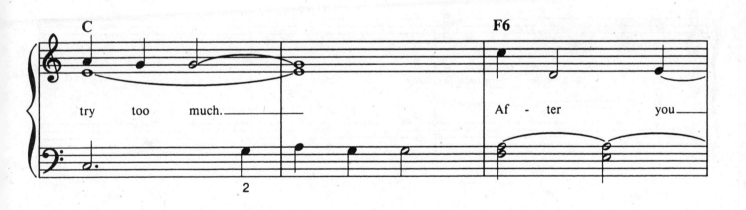

C / F6

try too much. Af - ter you

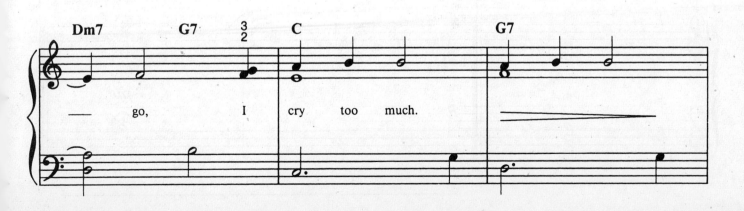

Dm7 / G7 / C / G7

go, I cry too much.

Love, look a - way.___ Lone - ly though I may

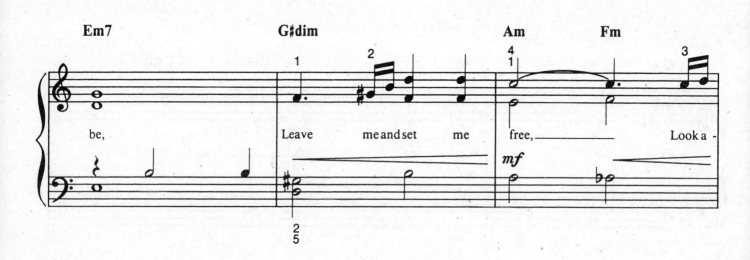

be, Leave me and set me free,___ Look a -

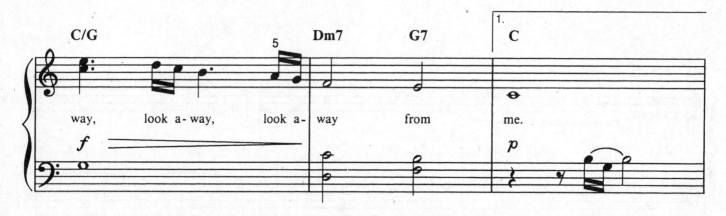

way, look a - way, look a - way from me.

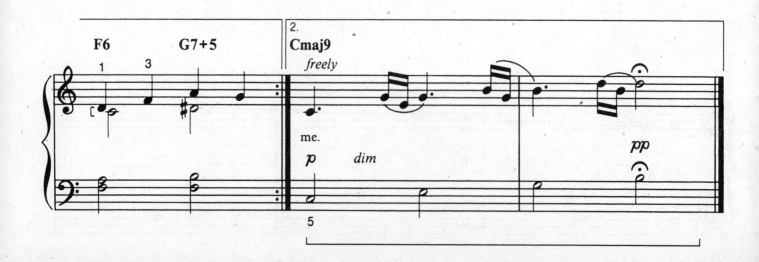

me.

MAMA, I'M A BIG GIRL NOW

from HAIRSPRAY

Music by MARC SHAIMAN
Lyrics by MARC SHAIMAN and SCOTT WITTMAN

Ma,___ I got-ta tell you that with-

out a doubt I get my best danc-ing les-sons from you - oo.___ You're_

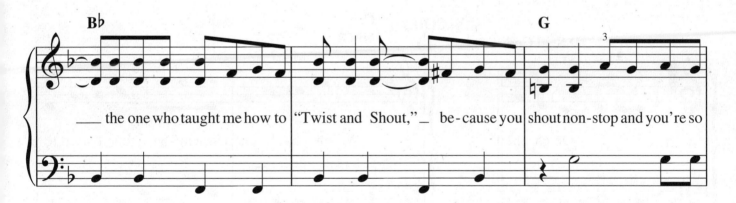

___ the one who taught me how to "Twist and Shout,"_ be-cause you shout non-stop and you're so

twist-ed___ too-oo! Wo - oh - oh - oh - oh! Once I used to fid-get 'cause I

just sat home.___ But now I'm just like Gid-get and I got-ta get to Rome!__ So

say *ar - ri - ve - der ci!* Too-dle- oo! And *ciao!*___ 'Cause ma-ma, I'm a big girl now!

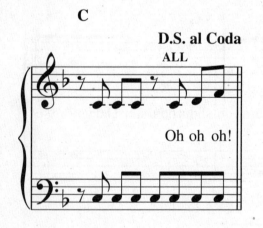

Oh oh oh!

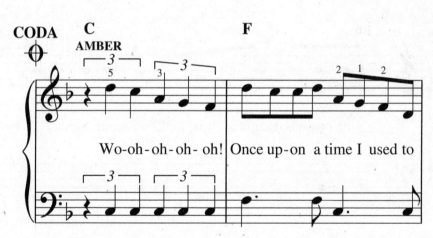

Wo-oh-oh-oh- oh! Once up-on a time I used to

dress up "Ken,"___ but now that I'm a wom-an I like big - ger men!___ And

Watch me fly!___ (Hey ma-ma, say, ma ma) One day I will meet a man you

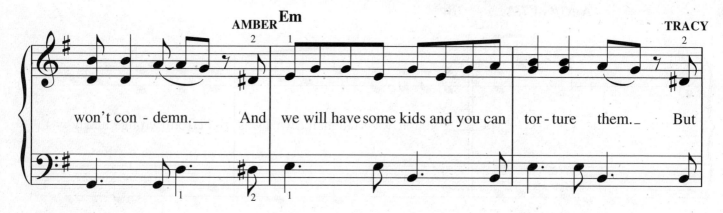

won't con-demn.___ And we will have some kids and you can tor-ture them._ But

let me be a star be-fore I take that vow,___ 'cause ma-ma, I'm a big girl now!

Oh - oh - oh! Ma-ma, I'm a big girl now! Hey - hey - hey - hey - hey!

MAMA SAYS
from the Broadway Musical FOOTLOOSE

Words by DEAN PITCHFORD
Music by TOM SNOW

With a bayou beat

(Spoken:) Now, Mama ain't been wrong yet, and I'm living proof.

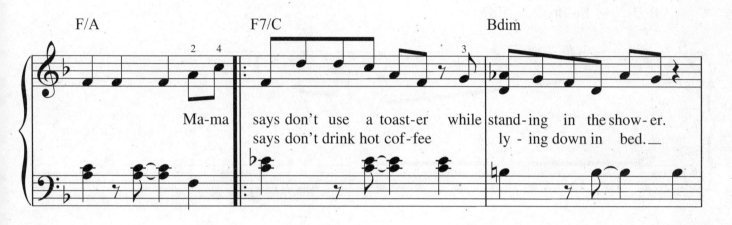

Ma-ma says don't use a toast-er while stand-ing in the show- er.
says don't drink hot cof-fee ly - ing down in bed.

Now who can ar - gue with that? Ma - ma
Don't e - ven give it a thought. Ma - ma

says don't hold your breath for long - er than an hour.
says nev - er eat an - y-thing that's big - ger than your head.

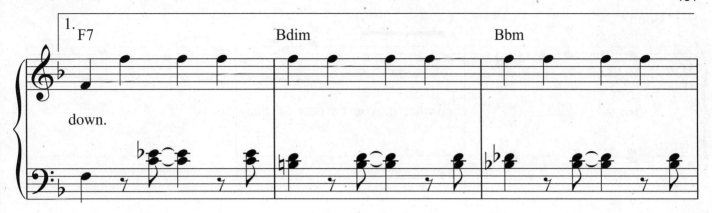

1. F7   Bdim   Bbm

down.

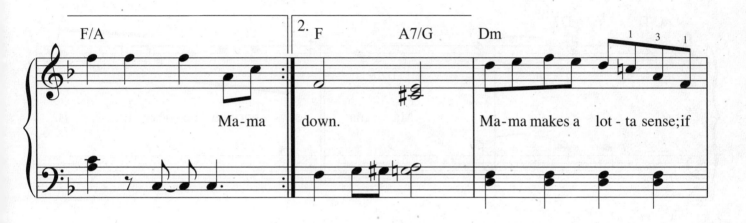

F/A   2. F   A7/G   Dm

Ma-ma   down.   Ma-ma makes a lot - ta sense; if

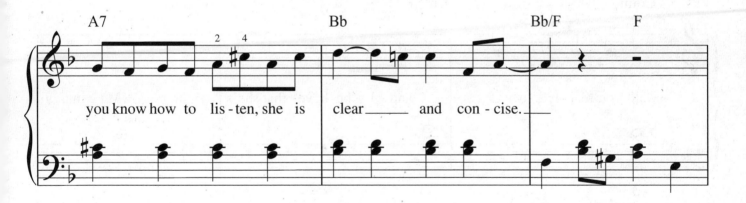

A7   Bb   Bb/F   F

you know how to lis - ten, she is clear____ and con - cise.____

Dm   A7   Bb

Dad-dy says, "I love her, son, but she's got mar-bles miss - in'." But I say, "Hey!_ It's

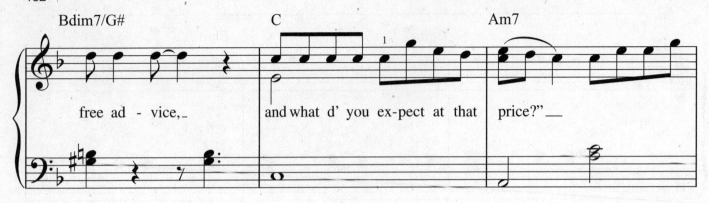

free ad - vice,_ and what d' you ex-pect at that price?"_

Freely

Ma - ma says what you be-lieve in____ is

all you real - ly own,_ and I be-lieve that she's right. Ma - ma

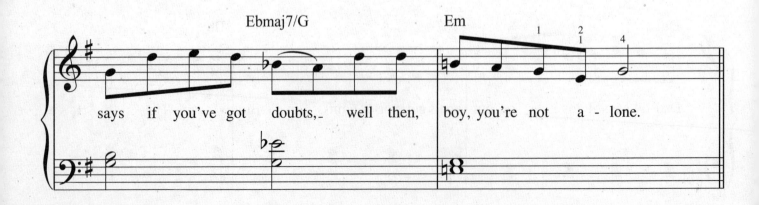

says if you've got doubts,_ well then, boy, you're not a - lone.

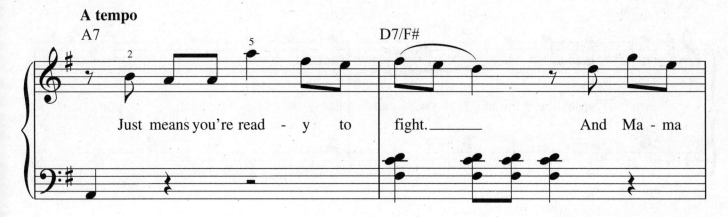

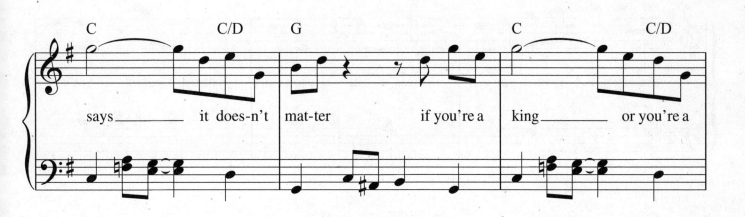

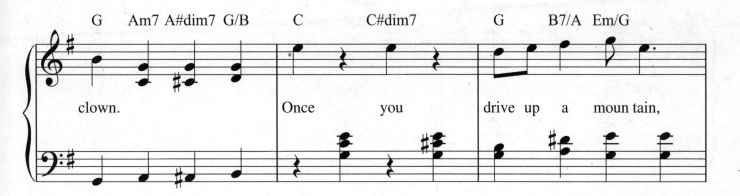

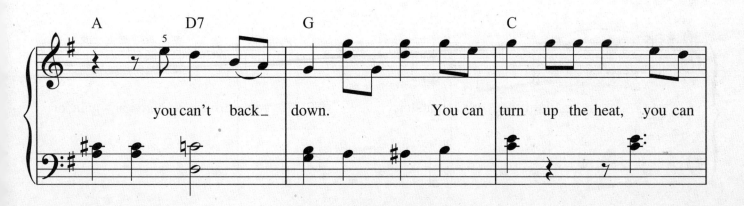

A tempo

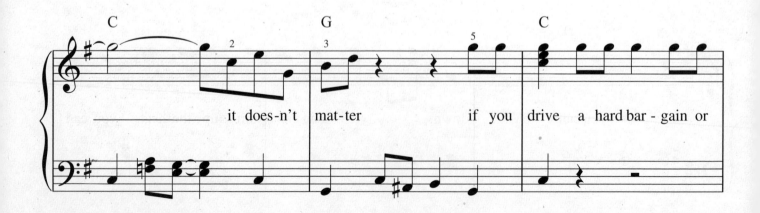

MAMMA MIA

from MAMMA MIA!

Words and Music by BENNY ANDERSSON,
BJORN ULVAEUS and STIG ANDERSON

1. I've been cheat-ed by you since I don't know when.
2. I've been an-gry and sad a-bout things that you do.

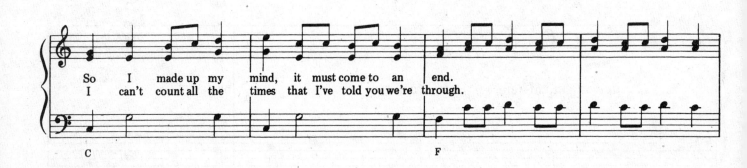

So I made up my mind, it must come to an end.
I can't count all the times that I've told you we're through.

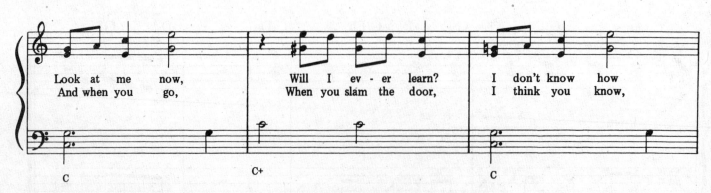

Look at me now,
And when you go,
Will I ev-er learn?
When you slam the door,
I don't know how
I think you know,

158

MATCHMAKER
from the Musical FIDDLER ON THE ROOF

Words by SHELDON HARNICK
Music by JERRY BOCK

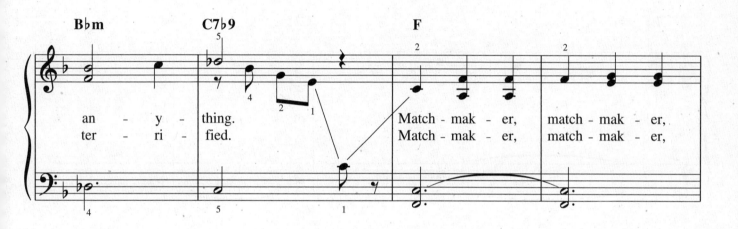

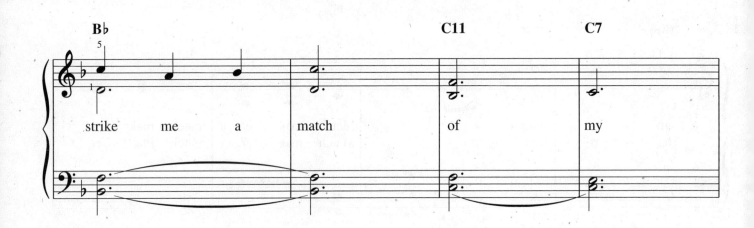

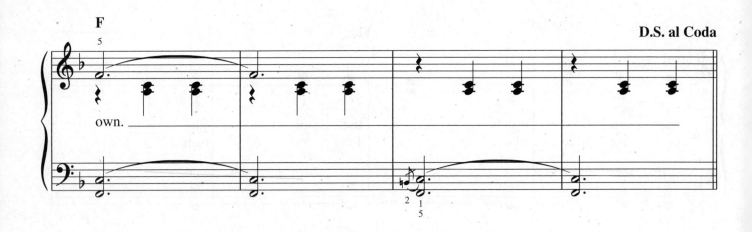

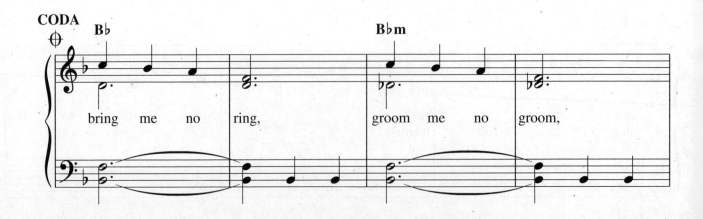

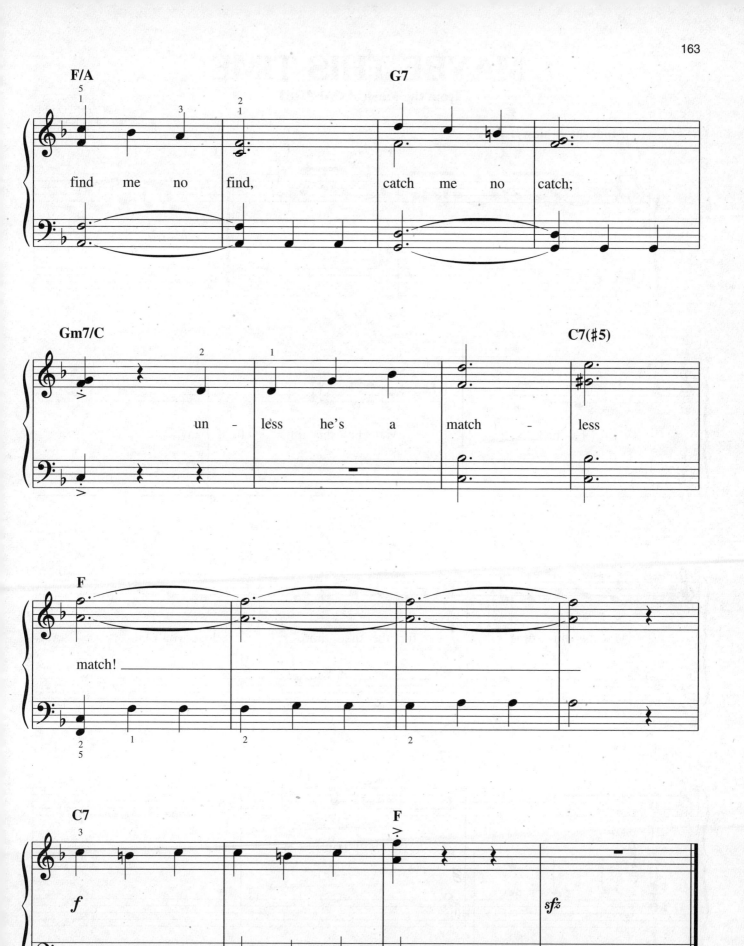

MAYBE THIS TIME

from the Musical CABARET

Words by FRED EBB
Music by JOHN KANDER

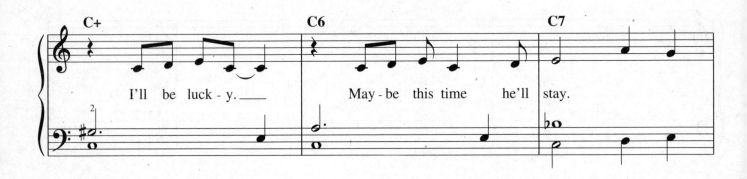

D7 **G13** **C7**

I'll be home at last. Not a los - er

F **Fm** **C** **Bb** **A7** **D7** **G7**

an - y - more, like the last time and the time be - fore. _

C **C+** **C6** **C7**

Ev - 'ry - bod - y __ loves a win - ner, __ so no - bod - y loved me.

F **F+** **F6** **F#dim7**

La - dy Peace - ful, _ La - dy Hap - py, _ that's what I long to be.

All the odds are — in my fa - vor;— some-thing's bound to be - gin.

It's got to hap - pen, — hap-pen some-time. — May-be this time I'll

5

win. Ev-'ry-bod-y ___ loves a win-ner,— so no-bod-y loved

me. La - dy Peace-ful, — La - dy Hap - py, —

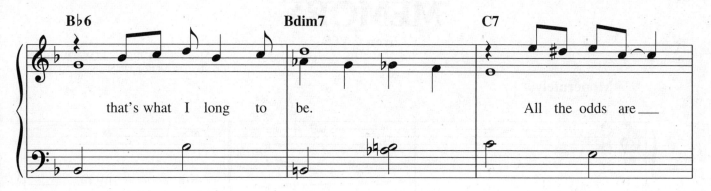

Bb6 that's what I long to be. **Bdim7** **C7** All the odds are___

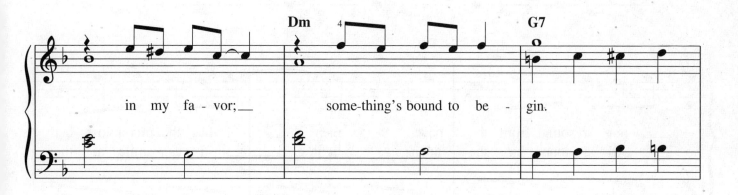

in my fa-vor;___ **Dm** some-thing's bound to be - gin. **G7**

F/C It's got to hap-pen, _ **F+/C#** hap-pen some-time. _ **Dm** May-be this time, _

G7 may-be **Gm7/C** this time I'll win. **F** **Db/F** **F**

MEMORY
from CATS

Music by ANDREW LLOYD WEBBER
Text by TREVOR NUNN after T.S. ELIOT

MONEY, MONEY

from the Musical CABARET

Words by FRED EBB
Music by JOHN KANDER

Moderately bright

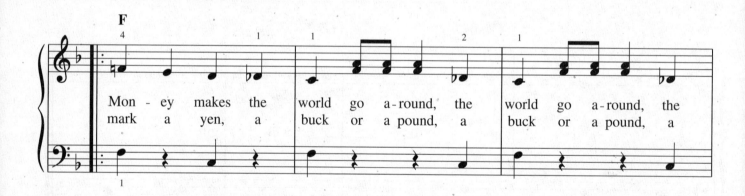

Mon - ey makes the world go a - round, the world go a - round, the
mark a yen, a buck or a pound, a buck or a pound, a

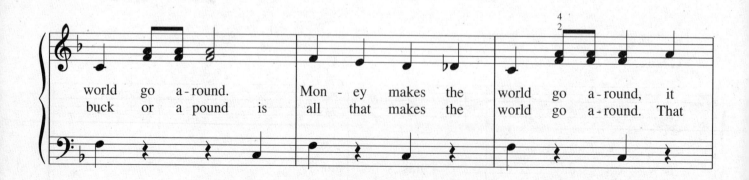

world go a - round. Mon - ey makes the world go a - round, it
buck or a pound is all that makes the world go a - round. That

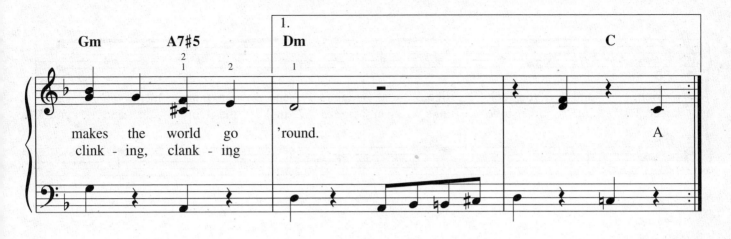

makes the world go 'round.
clink - ing, clank - ing

A

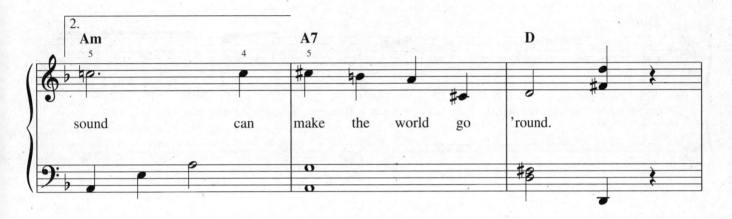

sound can make the world go 'round.

Mon - ey, mon - ey, mon - ey, mon - ey, mon - ey, mon - ey, mon - ey, mon - ey,

mon - ey, mon - ey, mon - ey, mon - ey.
mon - ey, mon - ey, mon - ey, mon - ey.

If you hap - pen to be
When you have - n't an - y

A7

rich, and you feel like a night's en - ter - tain - ment, you can
coal in the stove like and you freeze in the win - ter and you

Dm

pay for a gay es - ca - pade. If you hap - pen to be
curse to the wind at your fate. When you have - n't an - y

A7

rich and a - lone, and you need a com-pan - ion, you can
shoes on your feet and your coat's thin as pa - per and you

Dm   **N.C.**

ring ting - a - ling for the maid. If you hap - pen to be
look thir - ty pounds un - der - weight. When you go to get a

rich, and you feel you are left by your lov - er, though you
word of ad - vice from the fat lit - tle pas - tor, he will

moan and you groan quite a lot, you can take it on the
tell you to love ev - er - more. But when hun - ger comes to

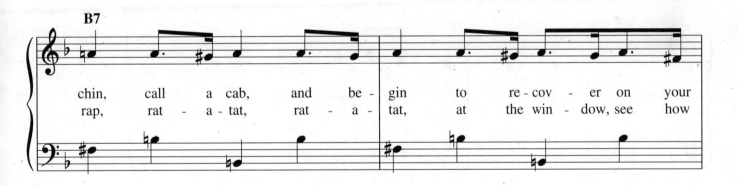

chin, call a cab, and be - gin to re - cov - er on your
rap, rat - a - tat, rat - a - tat, at the win - dow, see how

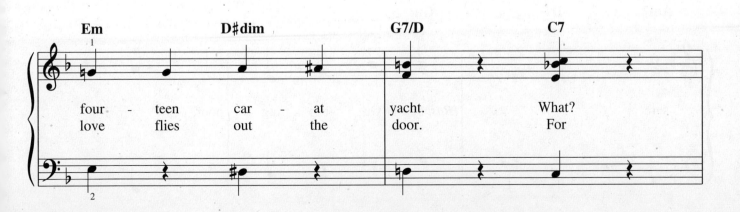

four - teen car - at yacht. What?
love flies out at the door. For

Mon - ey makes the world go a - round, the
mon - ey makes the world go a - round, the

world go a - round, the world go a - round.
world go a - round, the world go a - round.

1.

Gm   C7

Mon - ey makes the world go a - round; of that we both are

Am7   D7   Gm   C7   F

sure.   (Raspberry) On be - ing poor.

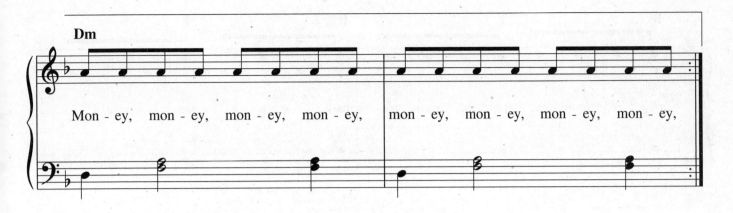

Dm

Mon - ey, mon - ey, mon - ey, mon - ey, mon - ey, mon - ey, mon - ey, mon - ey,

2.

Gm **C7**

Mon - ey makes the world go a - round. The clink - ing, clank - ing

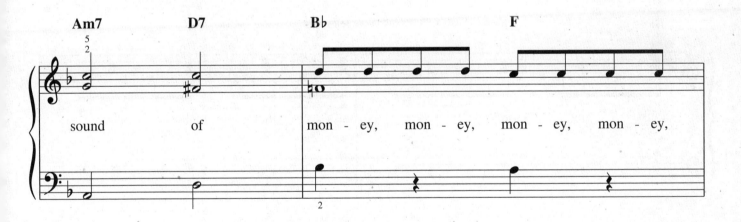

Am7 **D7** **B♭** **F**

sound of mon - ey, mon - ey, mon - ey, mon - ey,

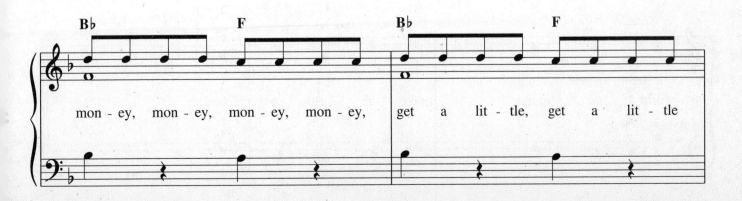

B♭ **F** **B♭** **F**

mon - ey, mon - ey, mon - ey, mon - ey, get a lit - tle, get a lit - tle

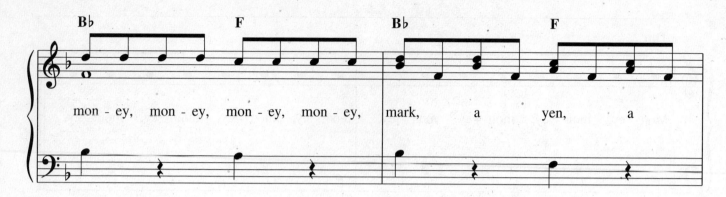

mon - ey, mon - ey, mon - ey, mon - ey, mark, a yen, a

buck or a pound, that clink - ing, clank - ing,

clunk - ing sound is all that makes the

world go 'round, it makes the world go 'round.

OKLAHOMA
from OKLAHOMA!

Lyrics by OSCAR HAMMERSTEIN II
Music by RICHARD RODGERS

Brand new state! Brand new

state, gon - na treat you great!

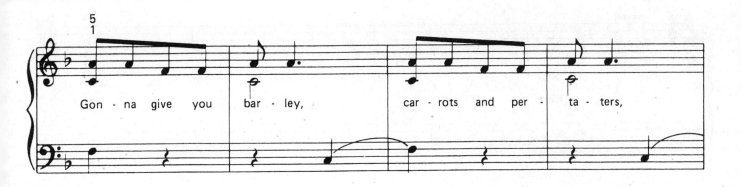

Gon - na give you bar - ley, car - rots and per - ta - ters,

Pas - ture fer the cat - tle, Spin - ach and ter - may - ters!

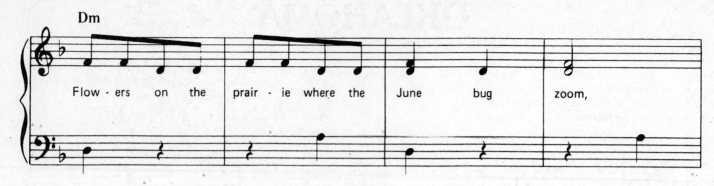

Flow - ers on the prair - ie where the June bug zoom,

Plen - 'y of air and plen - 'y of room,

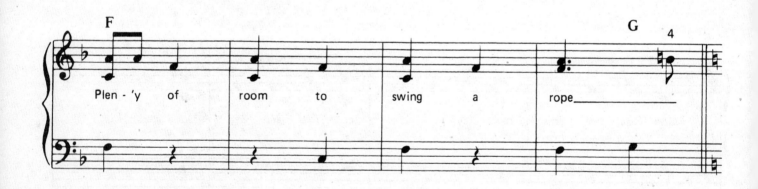

Plen - 'y of room to swing a rope____

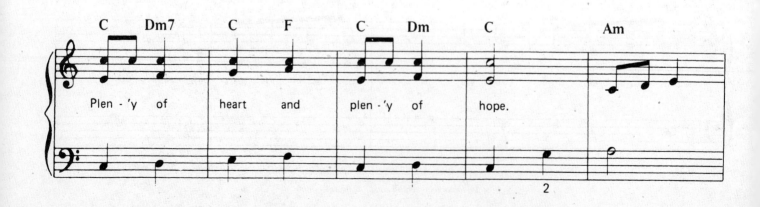

Plen - 'y of heart and plen - 'y of hope.

2

k - la - ho - ma, where the wind comes sweep-in' down the
k - la - ho - ma, Ev - 'ry night comes my hon - ey lamb and

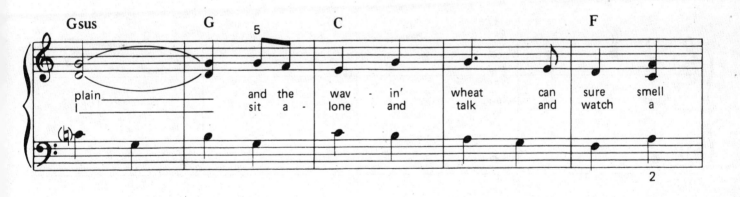

plain_____ and the wav - in' wheat can sure smell
I_____ sit a - lone and talk and watch a

sweet when the wind comes right be - hind the rain._____

hawk mak-in' la - zy cir - cles in the sky We

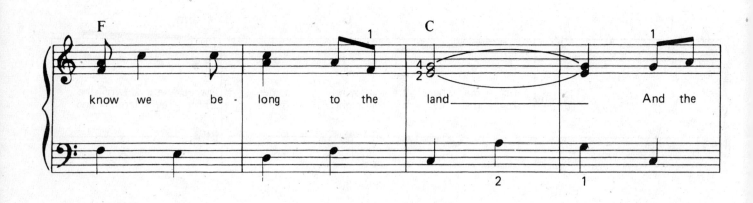

know we be - long to the land_____ And the

land we be - long to is grand! And when we

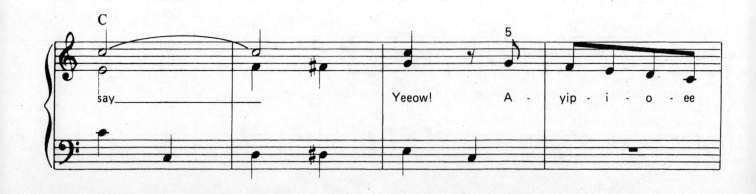

say_____ Yeeow! A - yip - i - o - ee

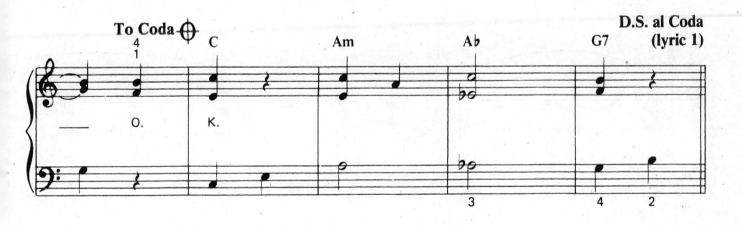

NO OTHER LOVE

from ME AND JULIET

Lyrics by OSCAR HAMMERSTEIN II
Music by RICHARD RODGERS

Slow Tango

Watch-ing   the   night   go   by,   Wish-ing   that   you   could

be   Watch-ing   the   night   with   me

In - to   the   night   I   cry,   hur - ry   home,   come

cresc.

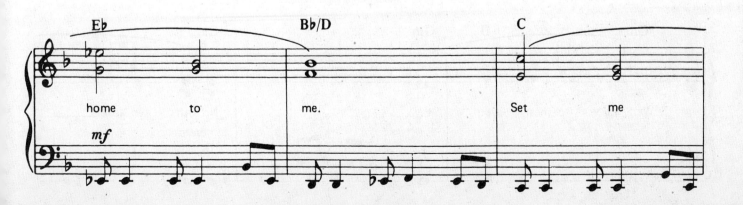

home   to   me.   Set   me

mf

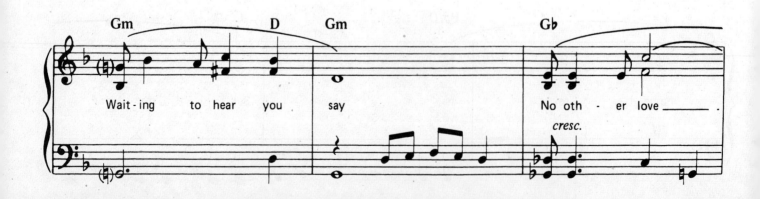

OL' MAN RIVER
from SHOW BOAT

Lyrics by OSCAR HAMMERSTEIN II
Music by JEROME KERN

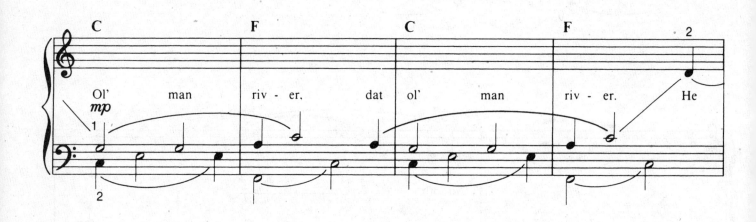

Ol' man riv-er, dat ol' man riv-er. He

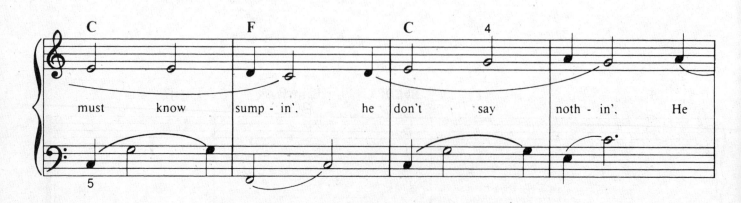

must know sump-in', he don't say noth-in', He

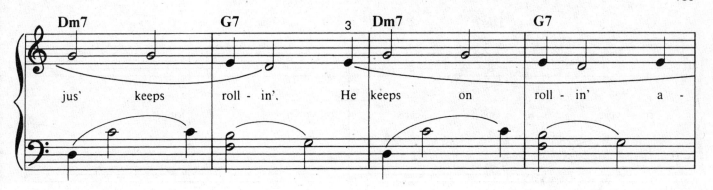

jus' keeps roll - in', He keeps on roll - in' a -

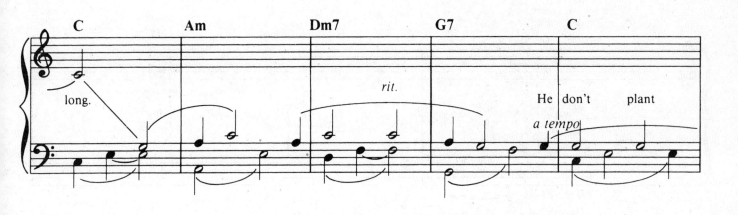

long. rit. He don't plant a tempo

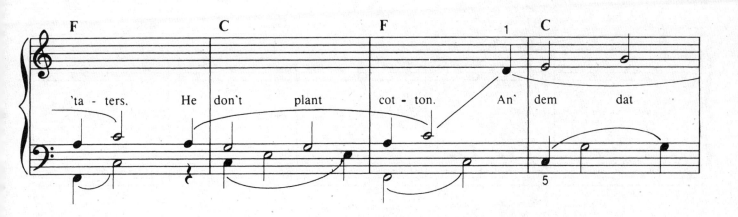

'ta - ters. He don't plant cot - ton. An' dem dat

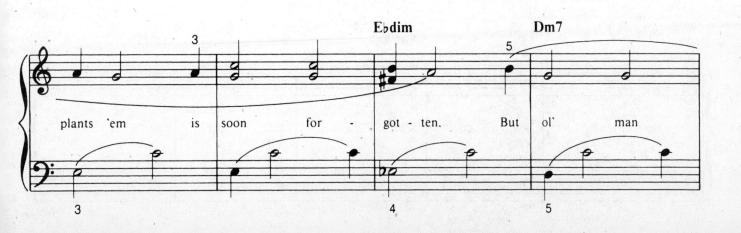

plants 'em is soon for - got - ten. But ol' man

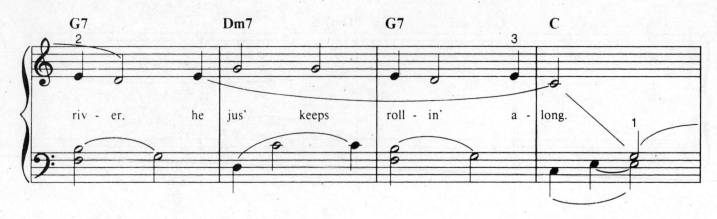

riv - er, he jus' keeps roll - in' a - long.

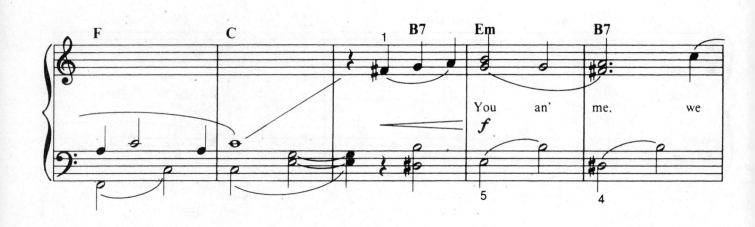

You an' me, we

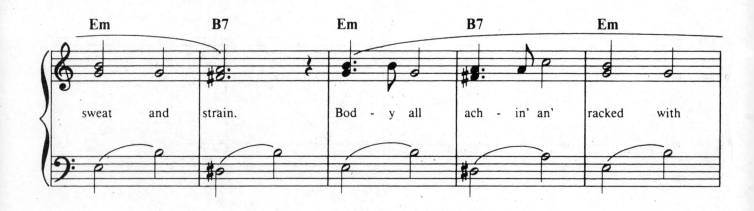

sweat and strain, Bod - y all ach - in' an' racked with

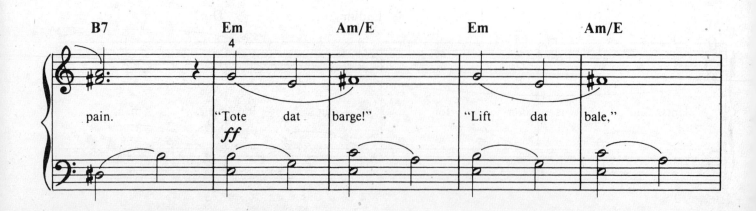

pain. "Tote dat barge!" "Lift dat bale,"

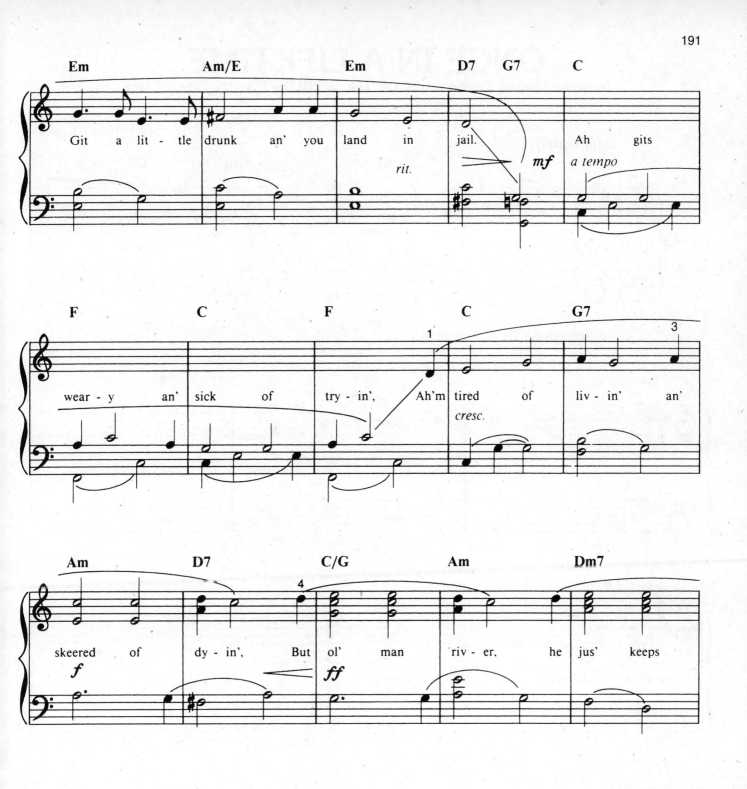

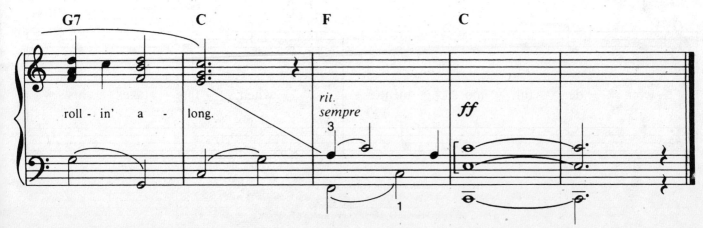

ONCE IN A LIFETIME

from the Musical Production STOP THE WORLD – I WANT TO GET OFF

Words and Music by LESLIE BRICUSSE
and ANTHONY NEWLEY

Just once in a life-time____ a

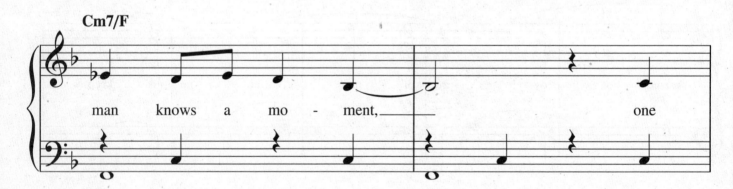

man knows a mo - ment,____ one

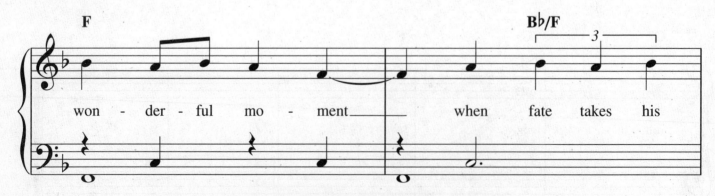

won - der - ful mo - ment____ when fate takes his

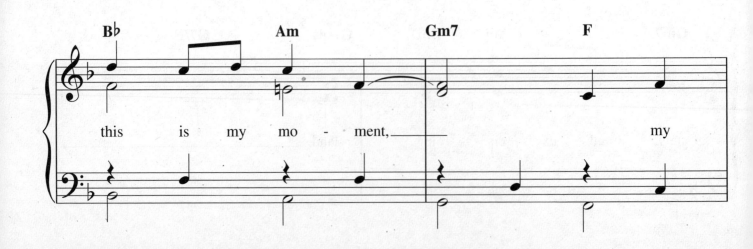

PEOPLE WILL SAY WE'RE IN LOVE
from OKLAHOMA!

Lyrics by OSCAR HAMMERSTEIN II
Music by RICHARD RODGERS

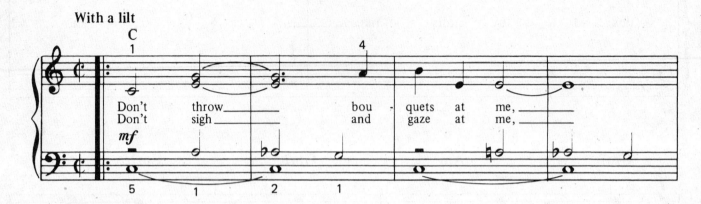

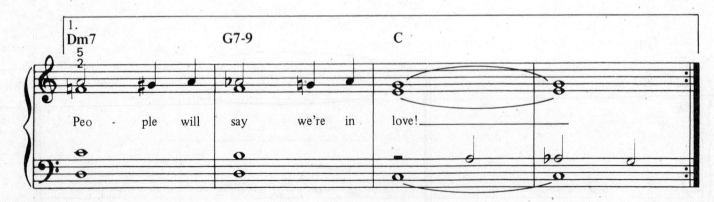

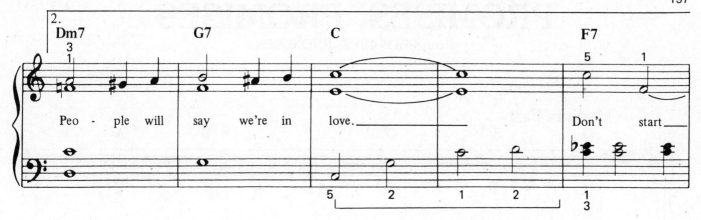

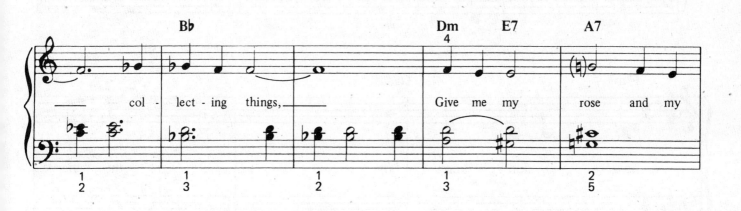

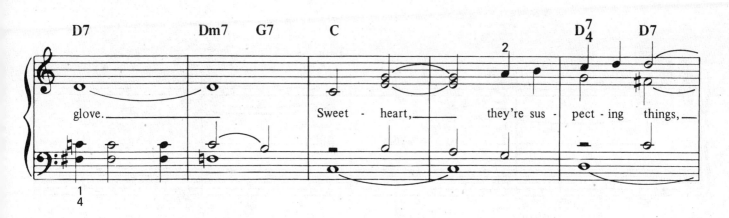

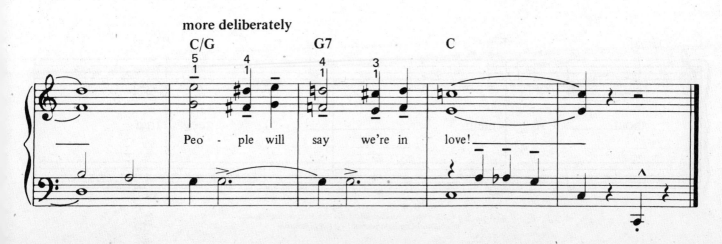

PROMISES, PROMISES

from PROMISES, PROMISES

Lyric by HAL DAVID
Music by BURT BACHARACH

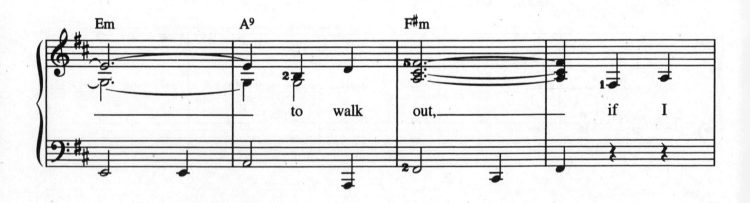

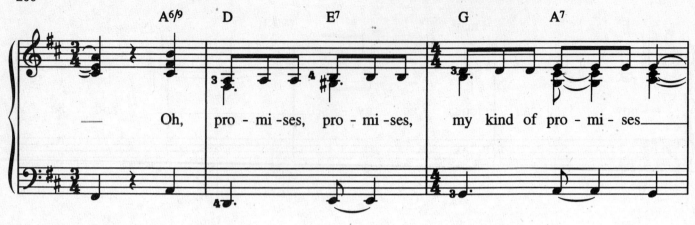

Oh, pro - mi -ses, pro - mi -ses, my kind of pro - mi - ses

can lead to joy and hope and

love: yes, love.

RIVER IN THE RAIN
from BIG RIVER

Words and Music by
ROGER MILLER

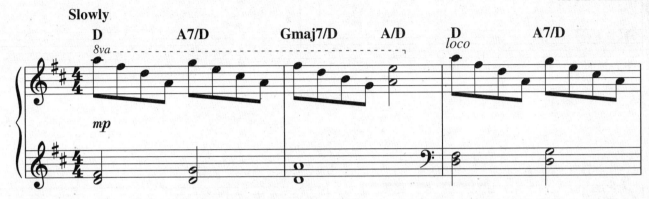

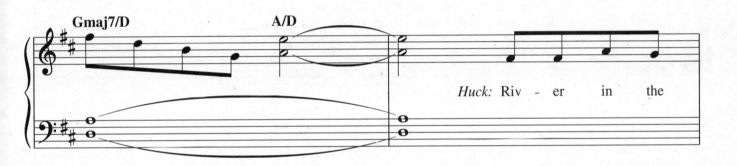

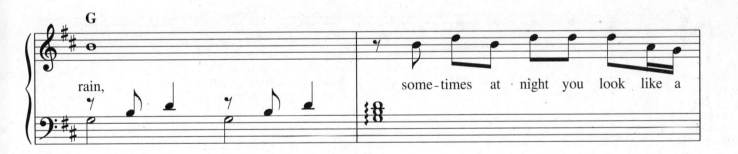

where.

Riv-er I love you. Don't you

care? If you're on the run

wind-in' some-place just tryin' to find the sun, __

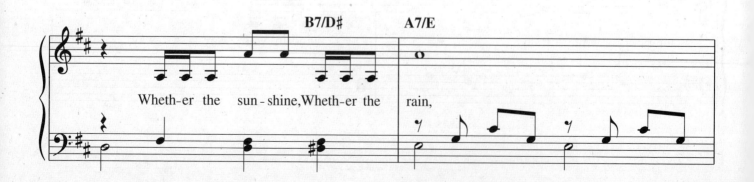

Wheth-er the sun-shine, Wheth-er the rain,

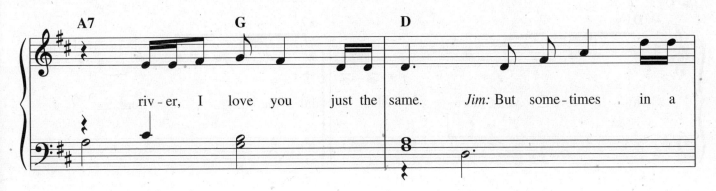

river, I love you just the same. *Jim:* But some-times in a

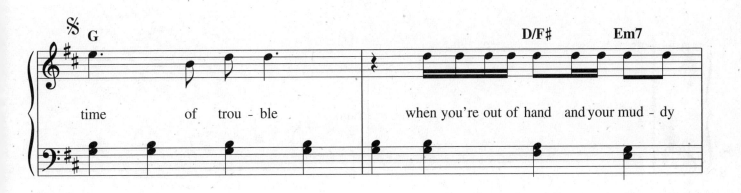

time of trou-ble when you're out of hand and your mud-dy

bub-bles roll a-cross my floor

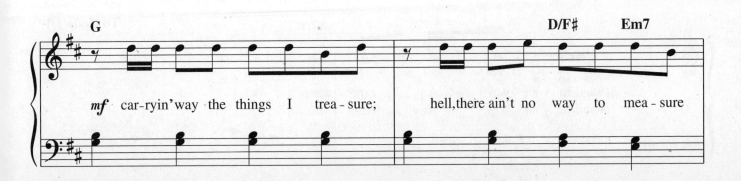

mf car-ryin' way the things I trea-sure; hell, there ain't no way to mea-sure

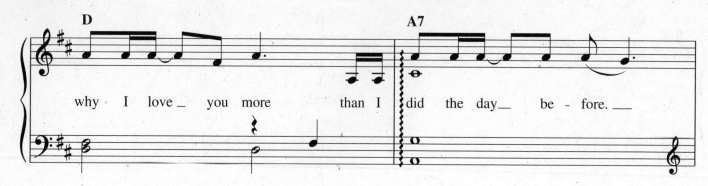

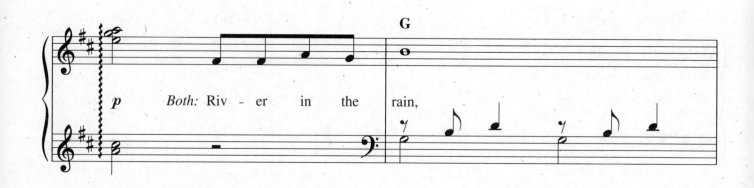

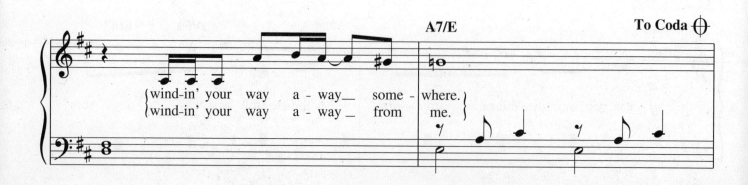

Riv-er, I love you. Don't you care? But some-times in a

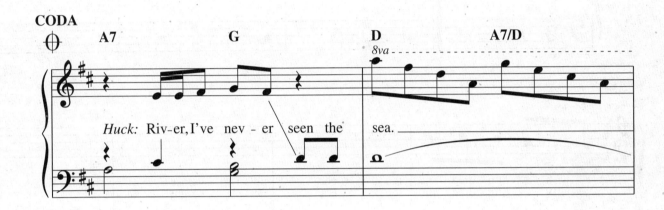

CODA

Huck: Riv-er, I've nev-er seen the sea.

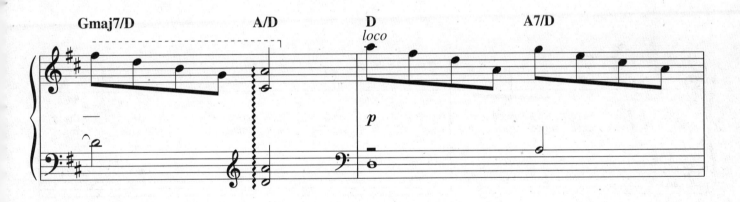

SEVENTY SIX TROMBONES

from Meredith Willson's THE MUSIC MAN

By MEREDITH WILLSON

March Tempo (♩. = 1 count)

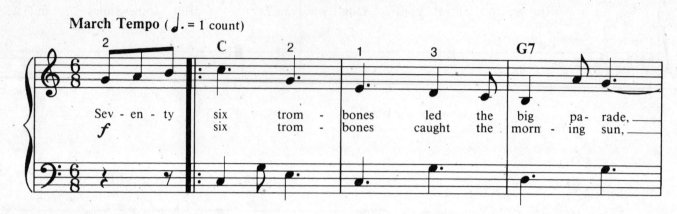

Sev - en - ty six trom - bones led the big pa - rade,
six trom - bones caught the morn - ing sun,

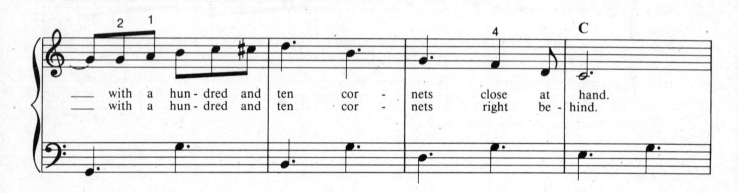

with a hun - dred and ten cor - nets close at hand.
with a hun - dred and ten cor - nets right be - hind.

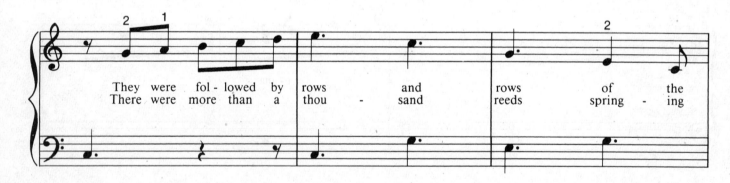

They were fol - lowed by rows and rows of the
There were more than a thou - sand reeds spring - ing

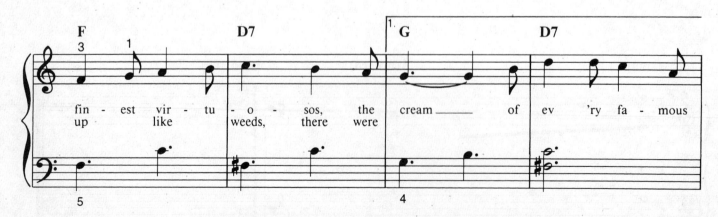

fin - est vir - tu - o - sos, the cream of ev 'ry fa - mous
up like weeds, there were

band. Sev - en - ty horns of ev - 'ry shape and

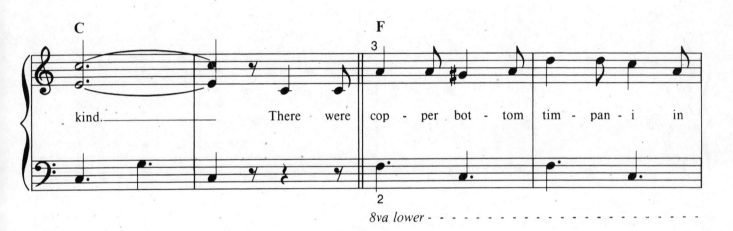

kind. There were cop - per bot - tom tim - pan - i in

8va lower -

horse pla - toons Thun - der - ing, thun - der - ing

all a - long the way. Dou - ble bell eu - phon - i - ums and

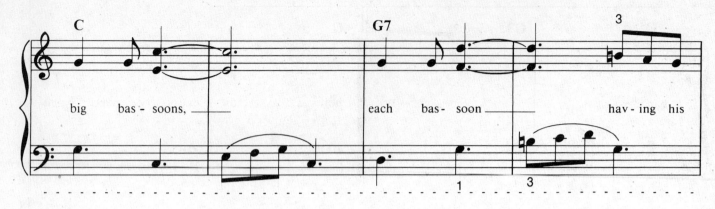

big bas - soons, _____ each bas - soon _____ hav - ing his

big fat say. There were fif - ty mount - ed can - on in the

bat - ter - y. _____ Thun - der - ing, thun - der - ing,

loud - er than be - fore. Clar - i - nets of ev - 'ry size and

trum - pet - ers who'd im - pro - vise a full oc - tave

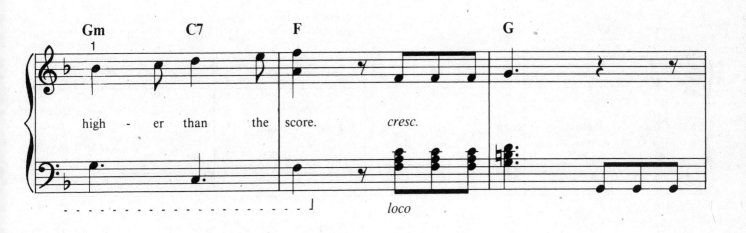

high - er than the score. *cresc.* *loco*

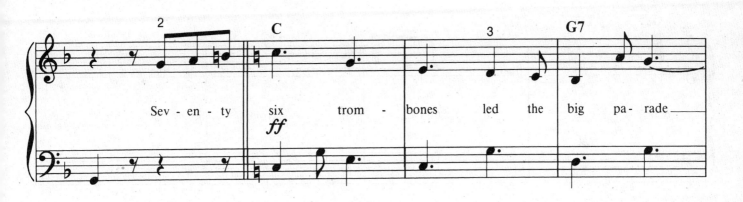

Sev - en - ty six trom - bones led the big pa - rade

ff

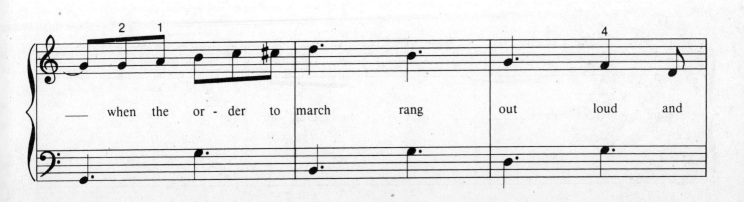

when the or - der to march rang out loud and

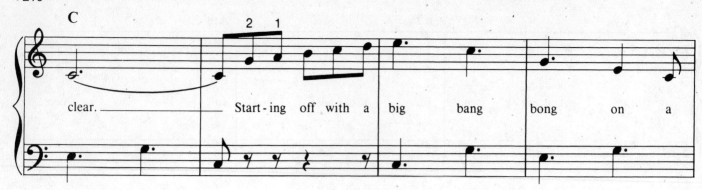

clear. _____ Start-ing off with a big bang bong on a

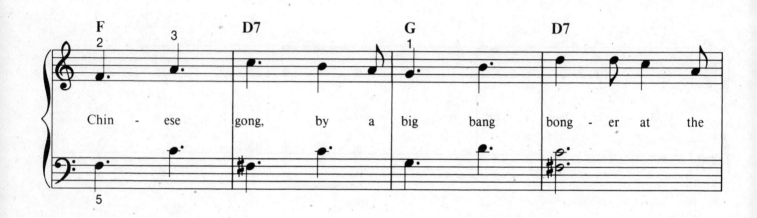

Chin - ese gong, by a big bang bong - er at the

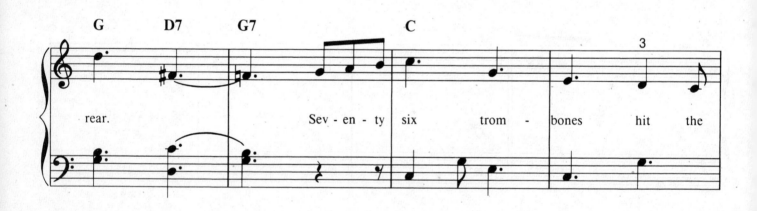

rear. Sev - en - ty six trom - bones hit the

coun - ter - point _____ while a hun - dred and ten cor -

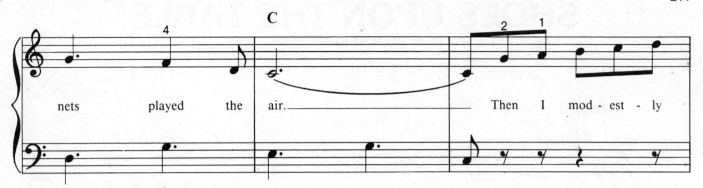

nets played the air._____ Then I mod - est - ly

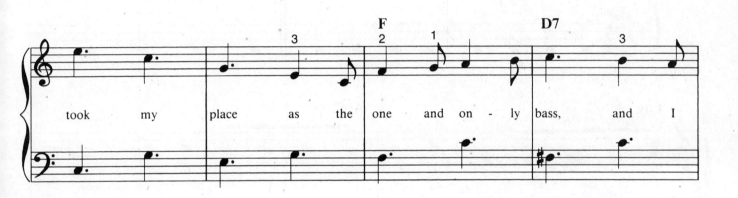

took my place as the one and on - ly bass, and I

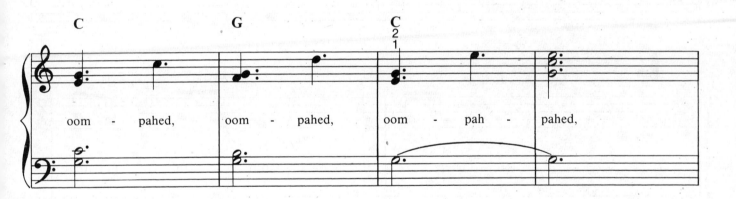

oom - pahed, oom - pahed, oom - pah - pahed,

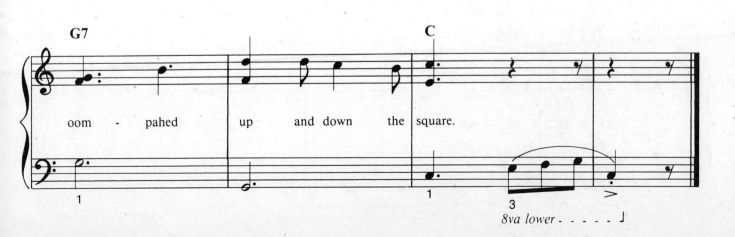

oom - pahed up and down the square.

8va lower - - - - -

SHOES UPON THE TABLE
from BLOOD BROTHERS

Words and Music by
WILLY RUSSELL

To Coda ⊕

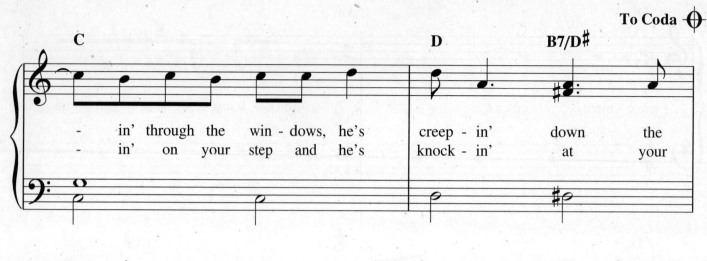

in' through the win-dows, he's   creep-in'   down   the
in' on your step and he's   knock-in'   at   your

hall.   Ain't no point in clutch-ing   at your

ro - sa - ry,___   you're   al - ways gon - na   know what was   done.___

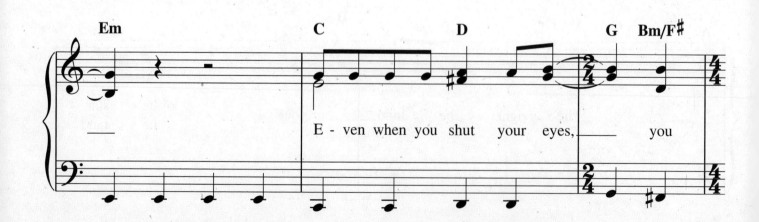

___   E - ven when you shut   your eyes,___   you

SIT DOWN YOU'RE ROCKIN' THE BOAT

from GUYS AND DOLLS

By FRANK LOESSER

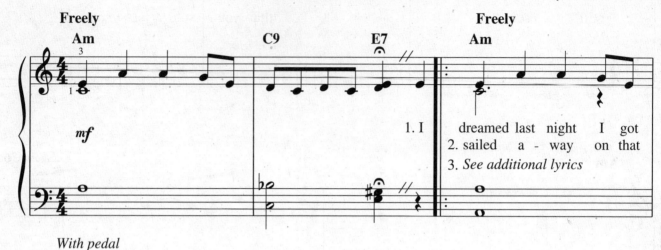

1. I dreamed last night I got
2. sailed a-way on that
3. *See additional lyrics*

With pedal

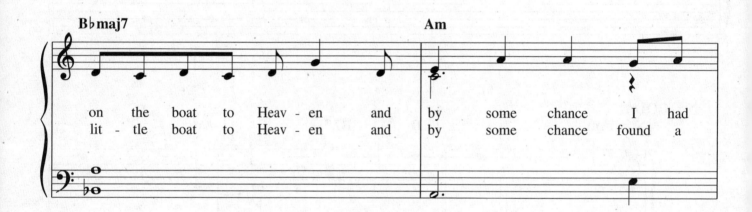

on the boat to Heav-en and by some chance I had
lit-tle boat to Heav-en and by some chance found a

brought my dice a-long. And there I stood and I
bot-tle in my fist. And there I stood nice-ly

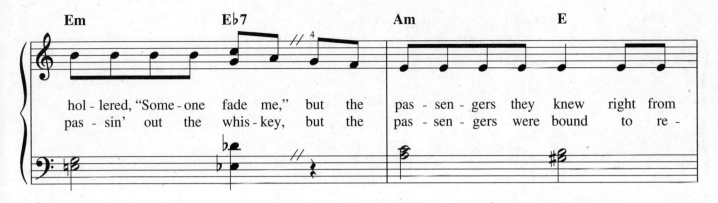

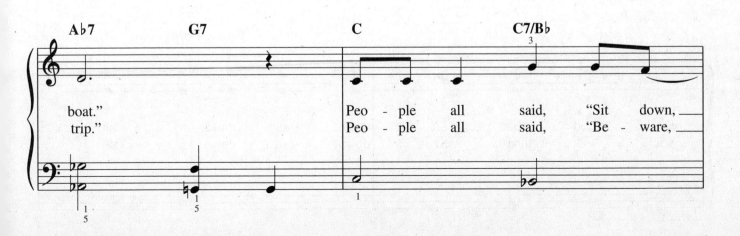

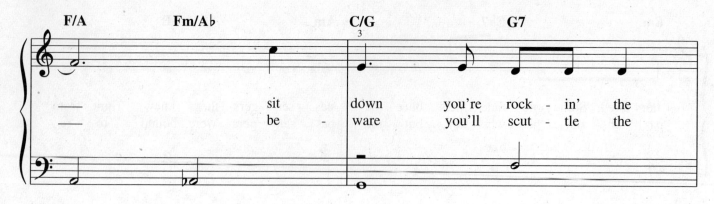

sit down you're rock - in' the
be - ware you'll scut - tle the

boat. And the dev - il will drag you
ship. And the dev - il will drag you

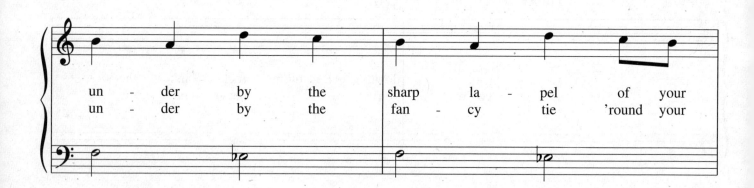

un - der by the sharp la - pel of your
un - der by the fan - cy tie 'round your

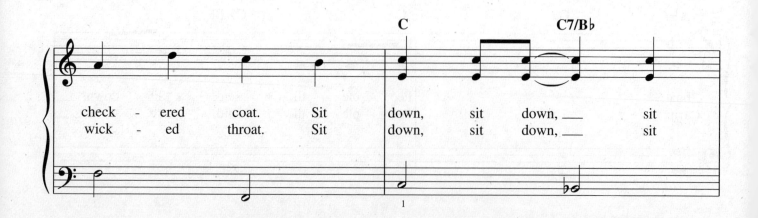

check - ered coat. Sit down, sit down, ___ sit
wick - ed throat. Sit down, sit down, ___ sit

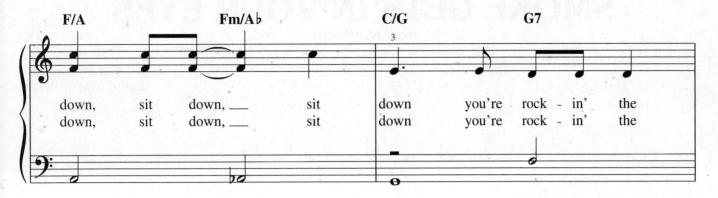

down, sit down, ___ sit down you're rock - in' the
down, sit down, ___ sit down you're rock - in' the

1.,2.

boat."
boat."

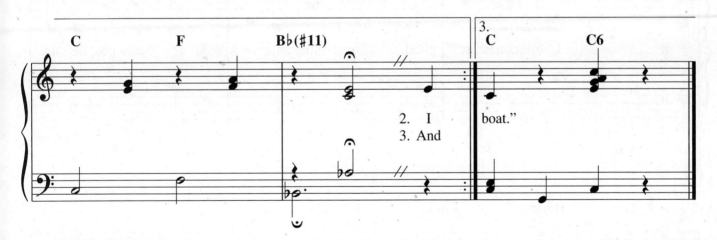

2. I
3. And

boat."

Additional Lyrics

3. And as I laughed at those passengers to Heaven
   A great big wave came and washed me overboard,
   And as I sank, and I hollered, "Someone save me,"
   That's the moment I woke up, thank the Lord.

   And I said to myself, "Sit down, sit down you're rockin' the boat."
   Said to myself, "Sit down, sit down you're rockin' the boat.
   And the devil will drag you under
   With a soul so heavy you'd never float.
   Sit down, sit down, sit down, sit down,
   Sit down, you're rockin' the boat."

SMOKE GETS IN YOUR EYES
from ROBERTA

Words by OTTO HARBACH
Music by JEROME KERN

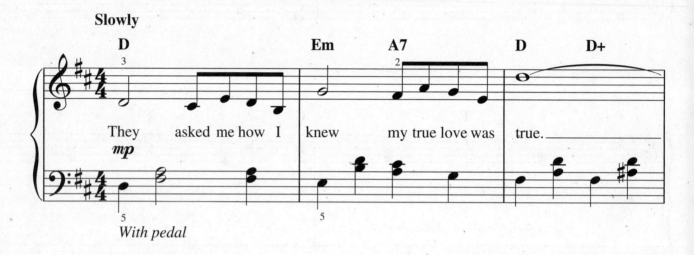

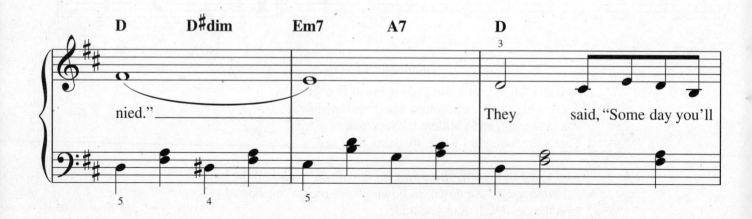

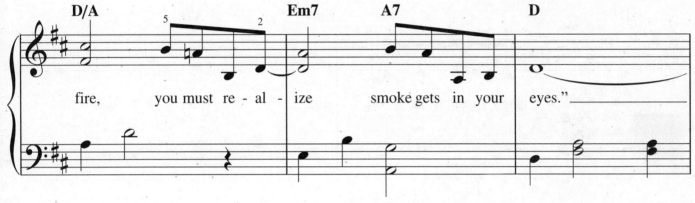

THE SOUND OF MUSIC
from THE SOUND OF MUSIC

Lyrics by OSCAR HAMMERSTEIN II
Music by RICHARD RODGERS

The hills are a-live _____ with the sound of mus - ic, with

songs they have sung _____ for a thou - sand years. _____ The

hills fill my heart _____ with the sound of mu - sic. _____ My

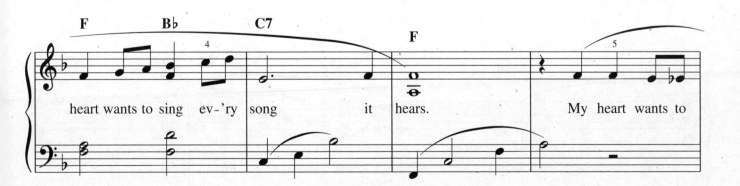

heart wants to sing ev-'ry song it hears. My heart wants to

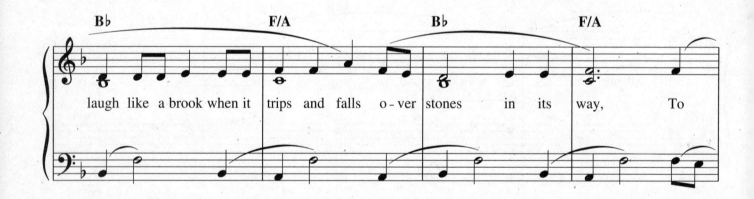

go to the hills _____ when my heart is lone - ly. I

know I will hear _____ what I've heard be - fore. _____ My

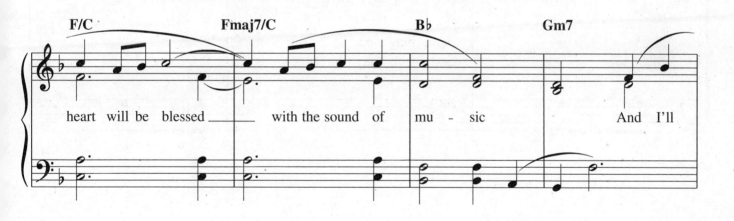

heart will be blessed _____ with the sound of mu - sic And I'll

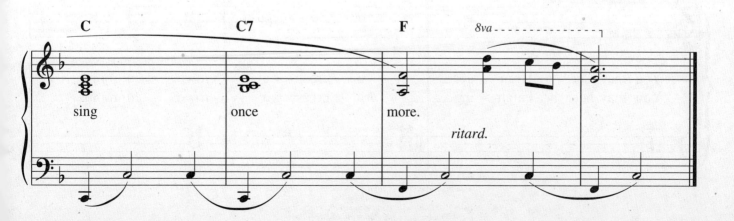

sing once more.

SOME ENCHANTED EVENING

from SOUTH PACIFIC

Lyrics by OSCAR HAMMERSTEIN II
Music by RICHARD RODGERS

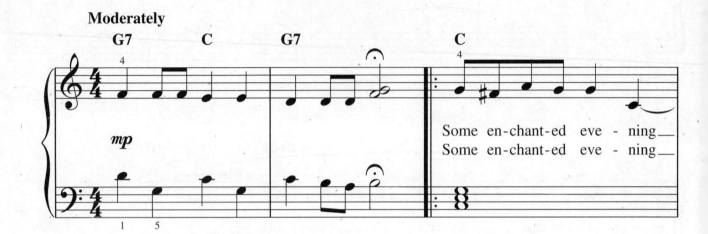

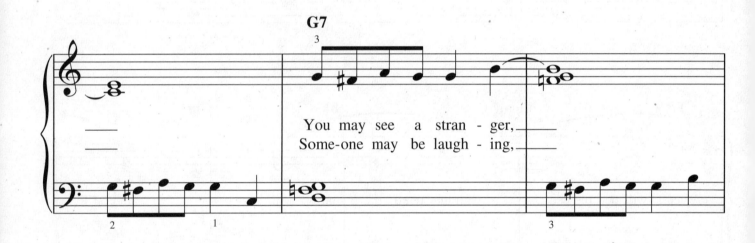

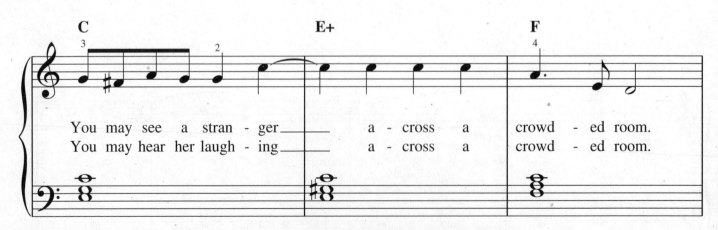

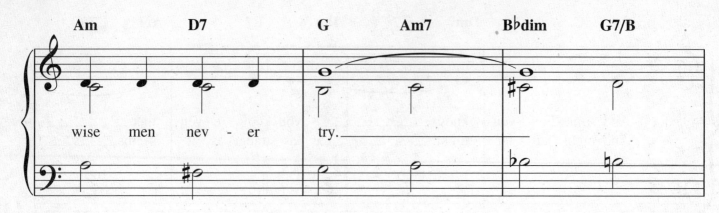

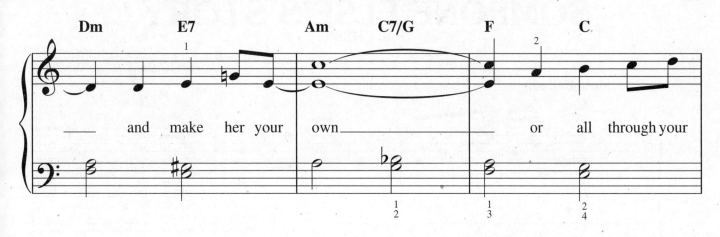

and make her your own _____ or all through your

life you may dream all a - lone. _____

Once you have found her, nev - er let her go. Once you have found her

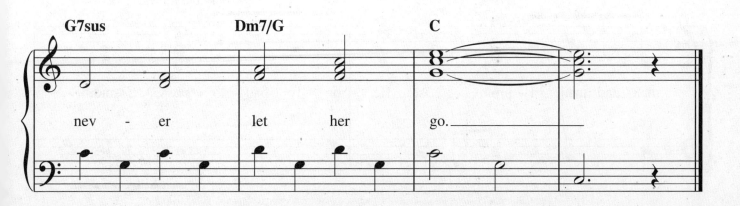

nev - er let her go. _____

SOMEONE ELSE'S STORY

from CHESS

Words and Music by BENNY ANDERSSON,
TIM RICE and BJORN ULVAEUS

SOMEONE LIKE YOU

from JEKYLL & HYDE

Words by LESLIE BRICUSSE
Music by FRANK WILDHORN

STAYIN' ALIVE
from the Broadway Musical SATURDAY NIGHT FEVER

Words and Music by ROBIN GIBB,
MAURICE GIBB and BARRY GIBB

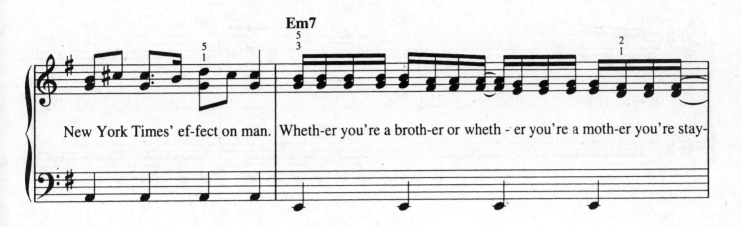

New York Times' ef-fect on man. | Wheth-er you're a broth-er or wheth - er you're a moth-er you're stay-

- in' a -live, __ stay-in'a-live. __ | Feel the cit-y break-in' and ev-'ry bod-y shak-in', and we're

stay-in' a - live, __ stay-in' a - live. __ | Ah, ha, ha, ha,

stay-in' a - live, __ stay-in' a - live. __ | Ah, ha, ha, ha,

Some-bod - y help me. _____ Some-bod - y help_ me yeah._

Life go-in' no - where._

Some-bod - y help_ me yeah._ Stay-in' a - live.

SUN AND MOON
from MISS SAIGON

Music by CLAUDE-MICHEL SCHÖNBERG
Lyrics by RICHARD MALTBY JR. AND ALAIN BOUBLIL
Adapted from original French Lyrics by ALAIN BOUBLIL

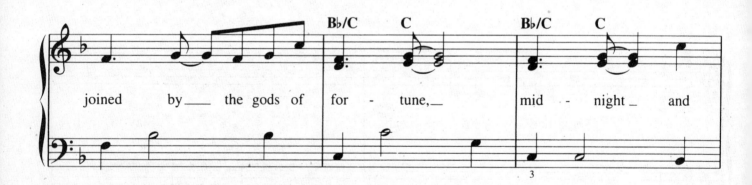

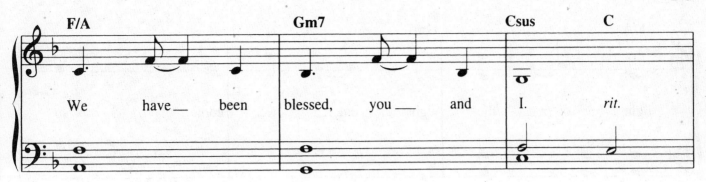

We have_ been blessed, you _ and I. *rit.*

CHRIS:

You are ___ here like _ a mys - t'ry._
a tempo

I'm from_ a world that's_ so dif - f'rent_ from

all that _ you are. How in _ the

light of ___ the night did ___ we come so

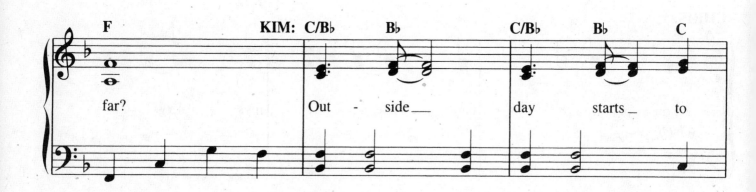

far? Out - side ___ day starts ___ to

dawn. Your moon ___ still floats ___ on

high. The birds a-wake. The stars shine, too. My

building in excitement

Bb7sus Bb7 CHRIS: Bb7sus Bb7 BOTH: Bb Bb7

hands   still shake.   I   reach   for you,   and we meet in the

Eb   Ab/Eb

sky.
ff

Ab/Bb Bb Ab/Bb Bb Gm Cm/G Cm Eb/Bb

Ab   Eb/G   Fm7   Bb7

rit.

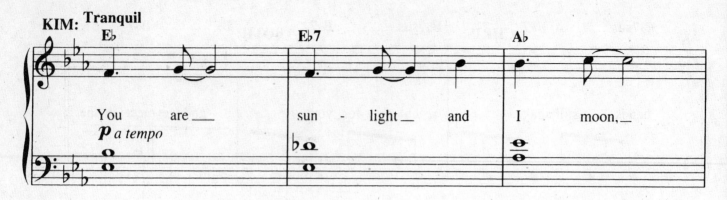

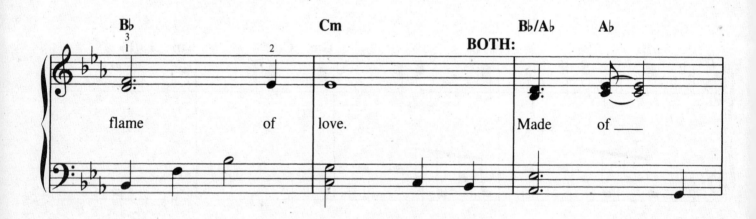

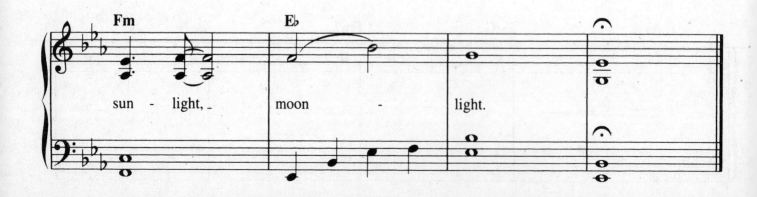

THE SURREY WITH THE FRINGE ON TOP
from OKLAHOMA!

Lyrics by OSCAR HAMMERSTEIN II
Music by RICHARD RODGERS

Easily, with a bounce

When I take you out to-night with

me _____ Hon-ey here's the

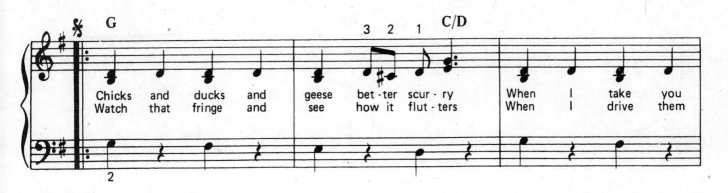

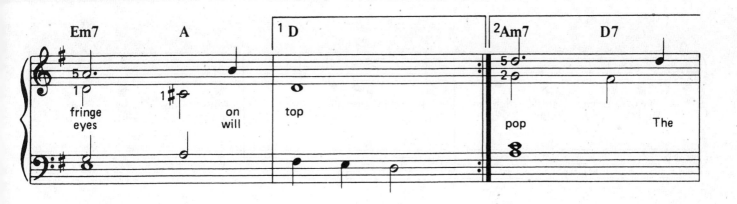

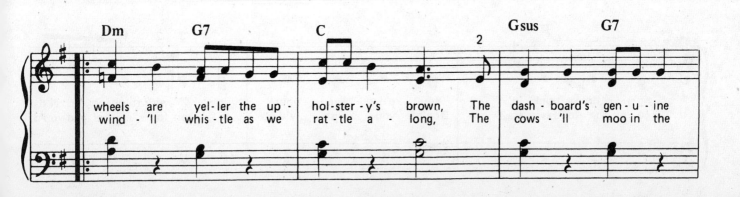

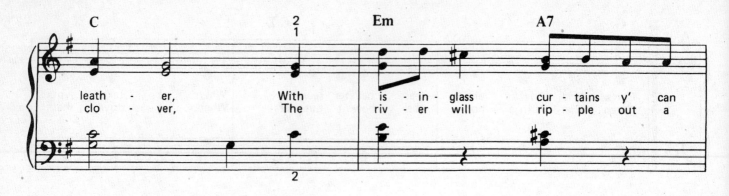

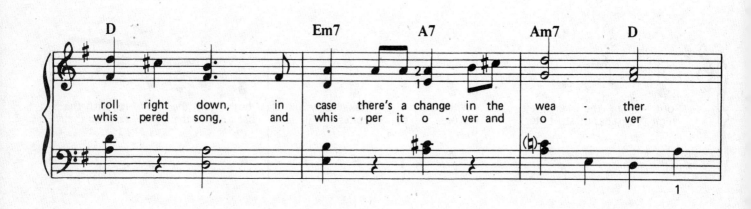

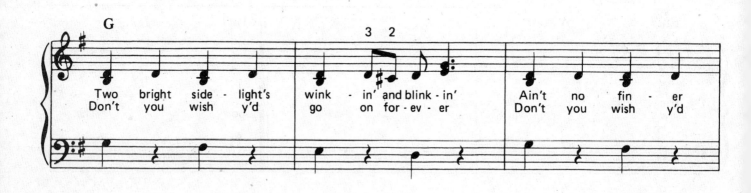

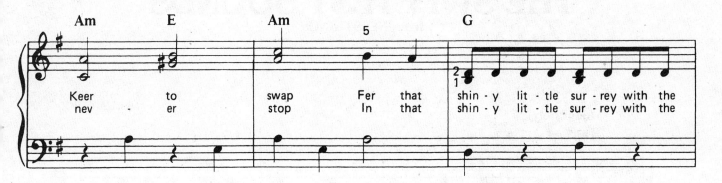

Keer — to
nev - er

swap
stop

Fer that
In that

shin - y lit - tle sur - rey with the
shin - y lit - tle sur - rey with the

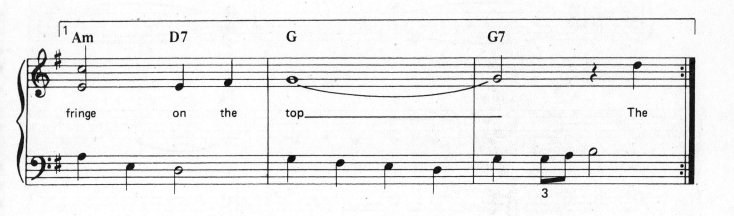

fringe

on the

top

The

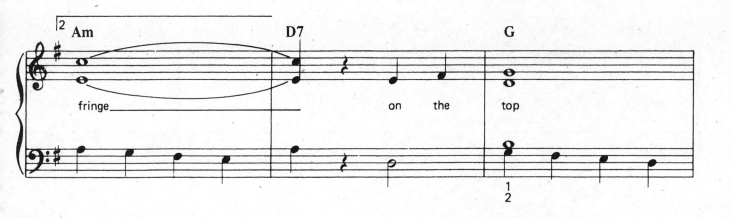

fringe

on the

top

THE SWEETEST SOUNDS
from NO STRINGS

Lyrics and Music by
RICHARD RODGERS

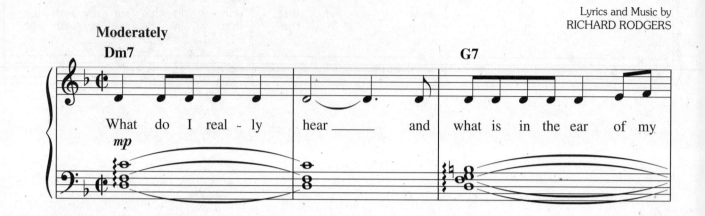

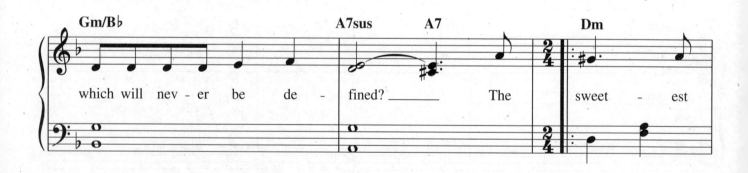

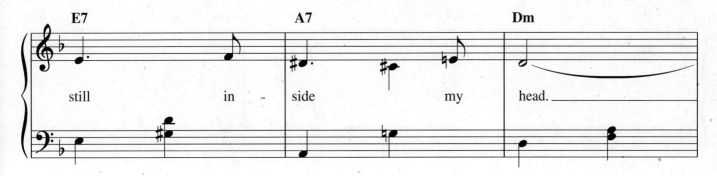

still in - side my head. _____

_____ The kind - est words I'll

ev - er know are wait - ing

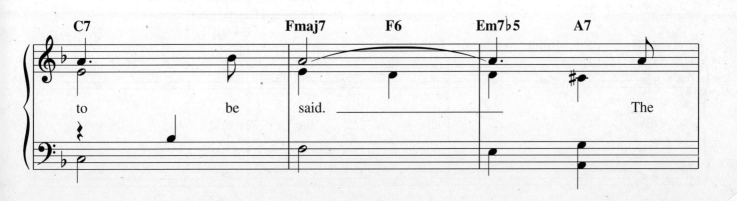

to be said. _____ The

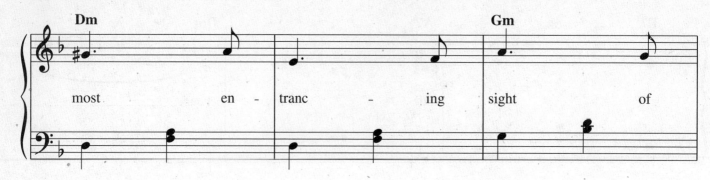

most en - tranc - ing sight of

all is yet for me to

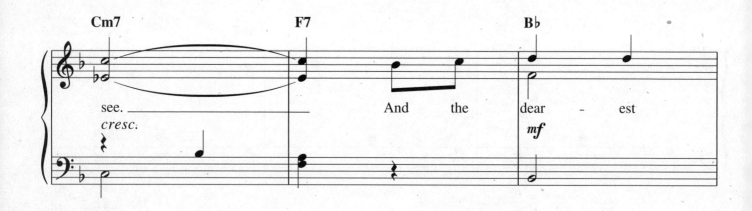

see. _____ And the dear - est

cresc.

love in all the world is

wait - ing   some - where   for   me.   Is

wait - ing   some - where,   some - where   for

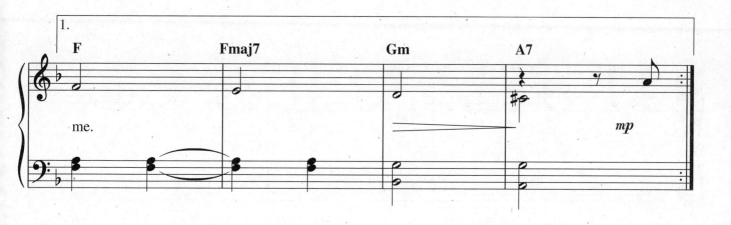

1.

me.

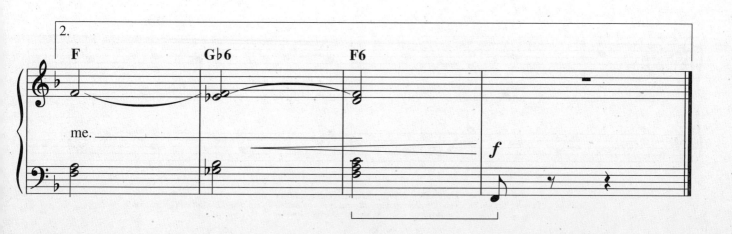

2.

me.

TEN CENTS A DANCE

from SIMPLE SIMON

Words by LORENZ HART
Music by RICHARD RODGERS

Slowly with a jazz feel

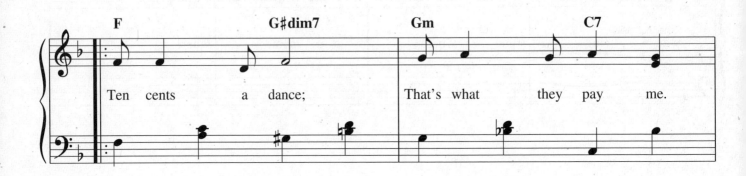

Ten cents a dance; That's what they pay me.

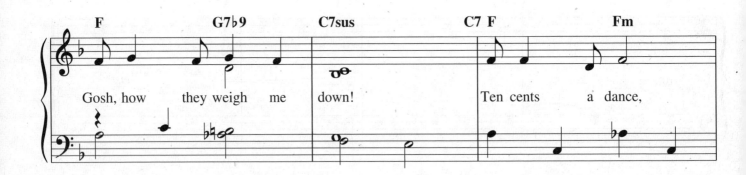

Gosh, how they weigh me down! Ten cents a dance,

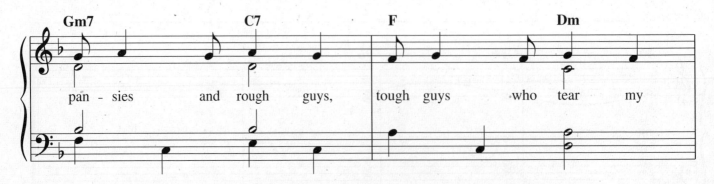

pan - sies and rough guys, tough guys who tear my

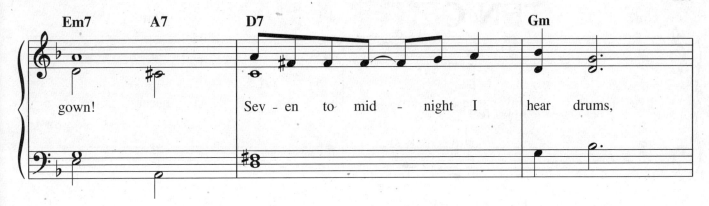

gown! Sev - en to mid - night I hear drums,

Loud - ly the sax - o - phone blows,

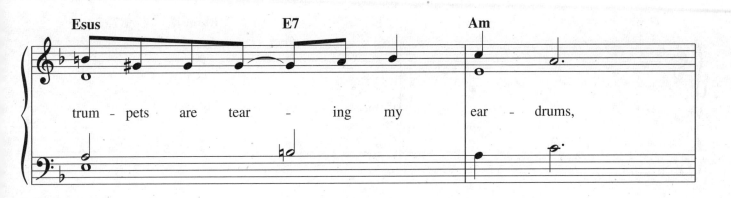

trum - pets are tear - ing my ear - drums,

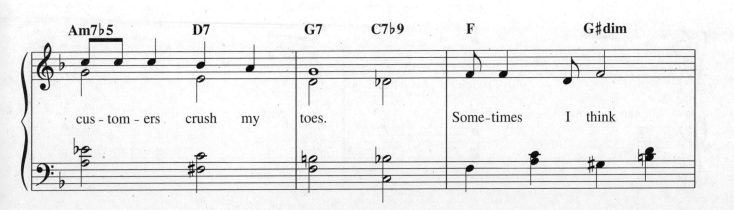

cus - tom - ers crush my toes. Some-times I think

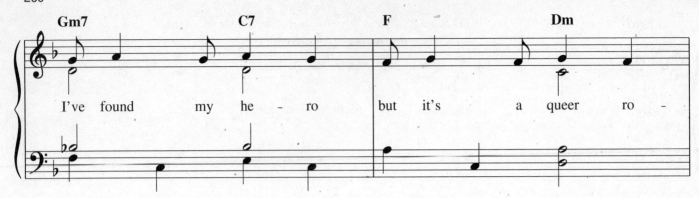

I've found my he - ro but it's a queer ro -

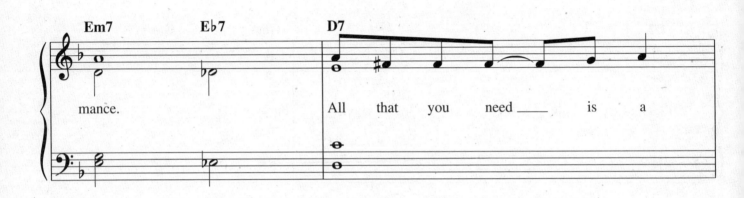

mance. All that you need ___ is a

tick - et. Come on big boy,

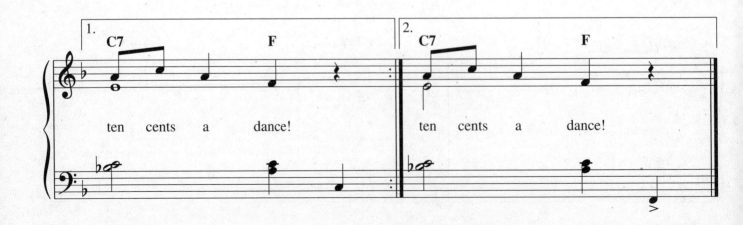

1. ten cents a dance!

2. ten cents a dance!

'TIL TOMORROW

from the Musical FIORELLO!

Lyrics by SHELDON HARNICK
Music by JERRY BOCK

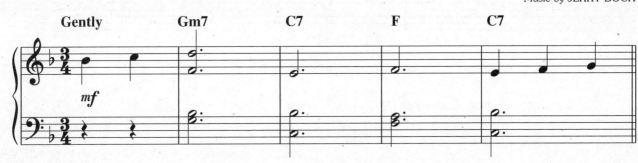

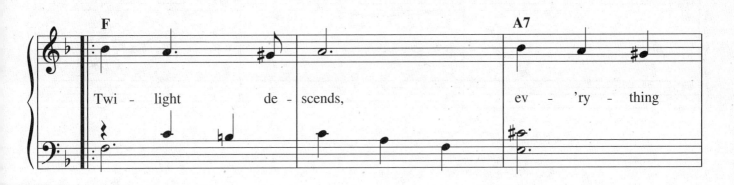

Twi - light de - scends, ev - 'ry - thing

ends 'til to - mor - row, _____ to -

mor - row. Since we must

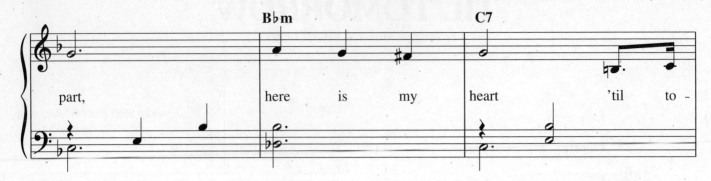

part, here is my heart 'til to-

mor - row, _____ to - mor -

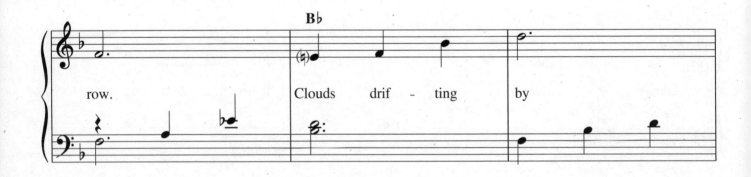

row. Clouds drif - ting by

ech - o a sigh, Part - ing is

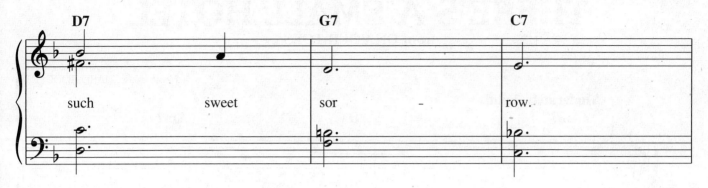

such   sweet   sor -   row.

I'm   drif - ting, too,   dream - ing   of

you   'til   to - mor -   row

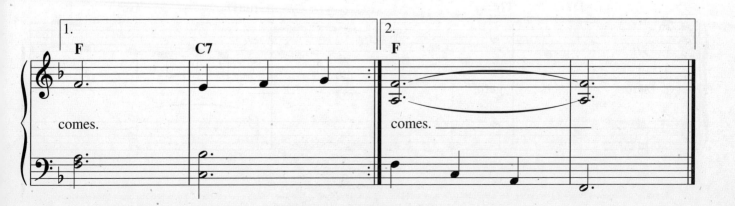

comes.   comes.

THERE'S A SMALL HOTEL

from ON YOUR TOES

Words by LORENZ HART
Music by RICHARD RODGERS

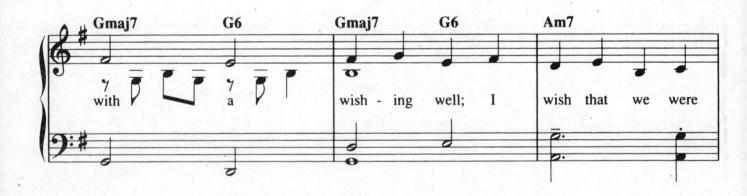

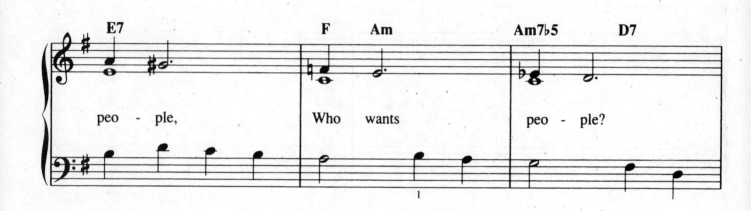

THIS IS THE MOMENT

from JEKYLL & HYDE

Words by LESLIE BRICUSSE
Music by FRANK WILDHORN

D.S. al Coda %

faced the world a - lone,

and now the time has come to

prove to them I made it on my own!

This is the

Coda

mo - ment,

the sweet - est mo - ment of them

all!

This is the mo - ment!

Damn all the

odds!

This day or nev - er, I'll set for - ev - er with the

THOROUGHLY MODERN MILLIE

from THOROUGHLY MODERN MILLIE

Words by SAMMY CAHN
Music by JAMES VAN HEUSEN

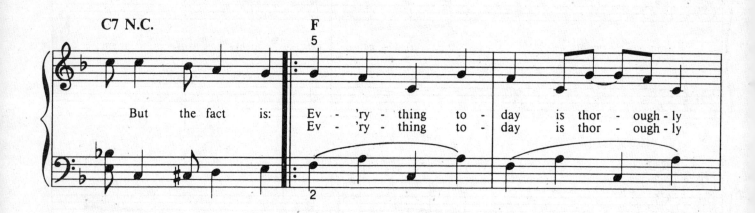

But the fact is: Ev - 'ry - thing to - day is thor - ough - ly
Ev - 'ry - thing to - day is thor - ough - ly

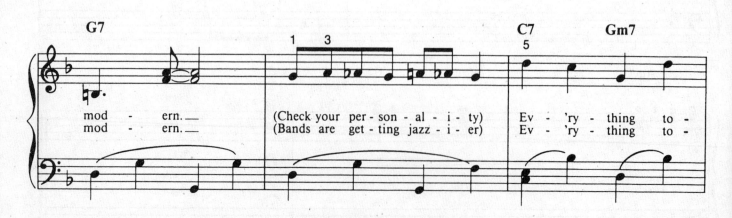

mod - ern.___ (Check your per - son - al - i - ty) Ev - 'ry - thing to -
mod - ern.___ (Bands are get - ting jazz - i - er) Ev - 'ry - thing to -

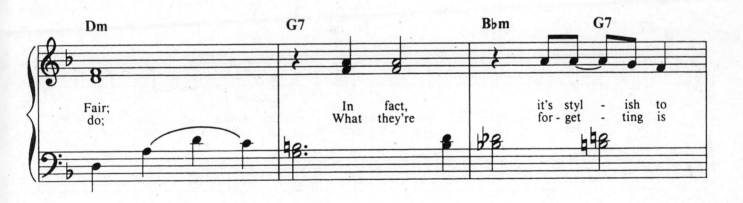

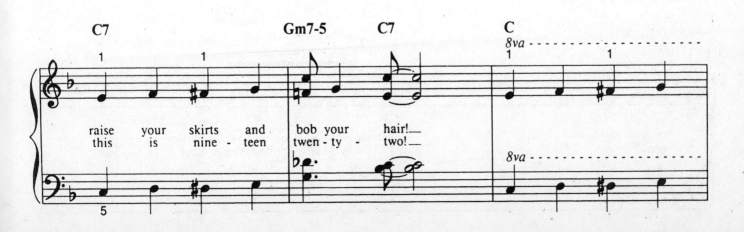

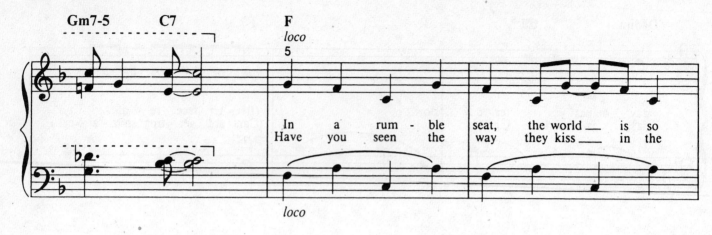

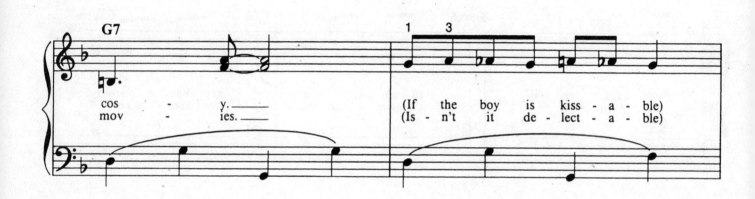

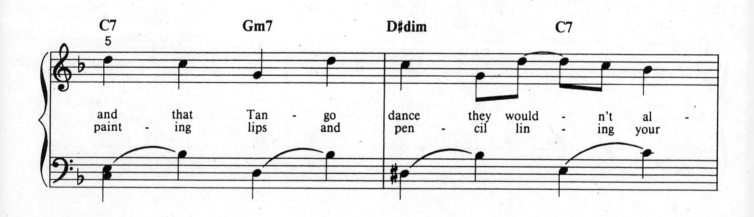

275

TILL THERE WAS YOU

from Meredith Willson's THE MUSIC MAN

By MEREDITH WILLSON

TURN BACK, O MAN

from the Musical GODSPELL

Words and Music by
STEPHEN SCHWARTZ

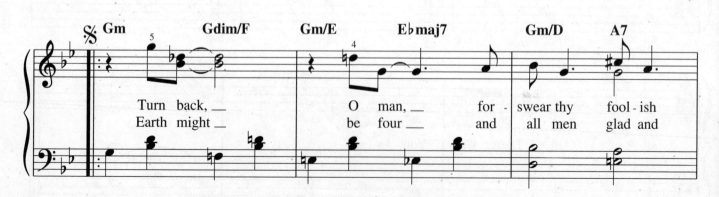

Turn back, __ O man, __ for - swear thy fool - ish

Earth might __ be four __ and all men glad and

D   G7   Ab7

ways   old now is   Earth and none may
wise   age af-ter   age, their tra-gic

Cm6   D7   Gm   Gdim/F

count her days.   Da da da da da   Yet thou, __
em-pires rise.   Built while __

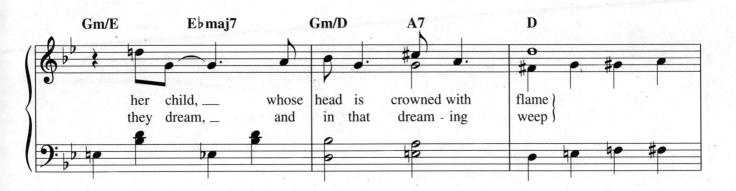

Gm/E   Ebmaj7   Gm/D   A7   D

her child, __   whose head is crowned with   flame
they dream, __   and in that dream-ing   weep

G7   Ab7   D7sus   D7#5

still walk not   hear _____ thine in-ner God pro-claim: __

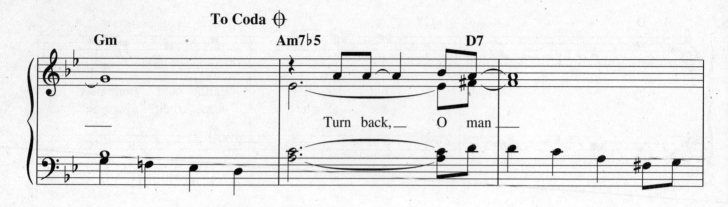

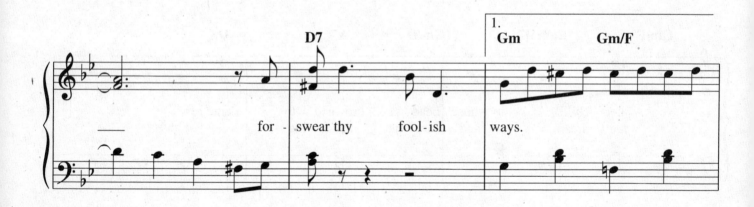

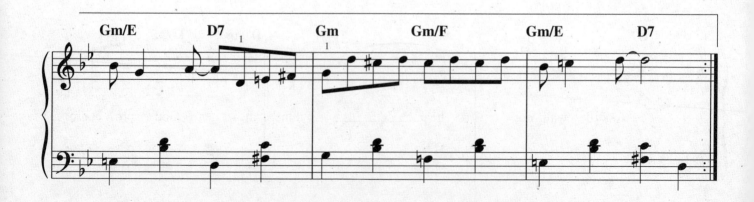

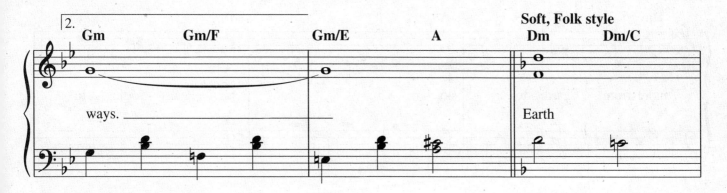

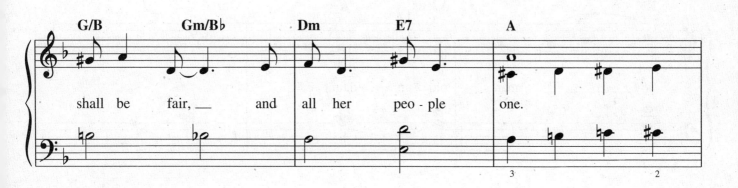

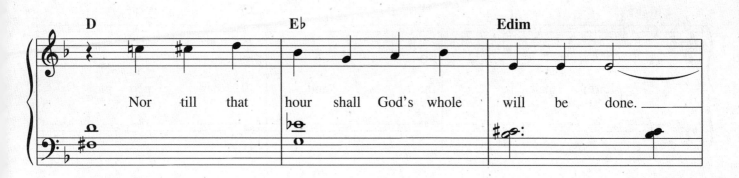

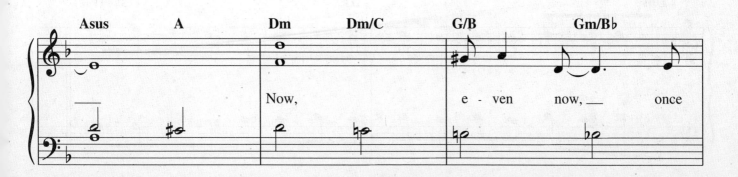

more from earth to sky. Peals forth in

joy _____ man's old un - daunt - ed cry:

Earth shall be fair, and all her peo - ple

one.

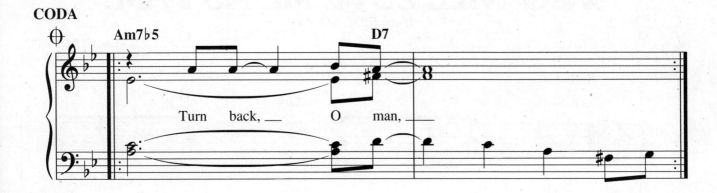

WHO WILL LOVE ME AS I AM?

from SIDE SHOW

Words by BILL RUSSELL
Music by HENRY KRIEGER

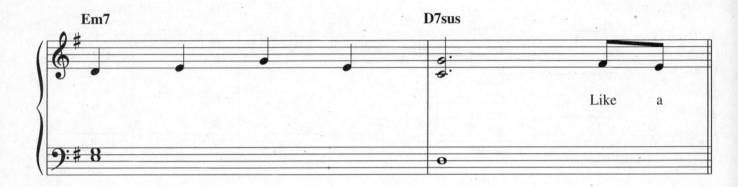

Like a

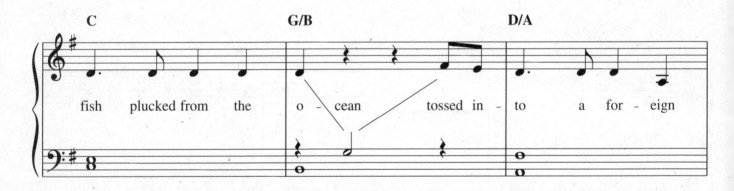

fish plucked from the o - cean tossed in - to a for - eign

stream, al - ways knew that I was dif - f'rent of - ten

fled in - to a dream. I ig - nored the rag - ing

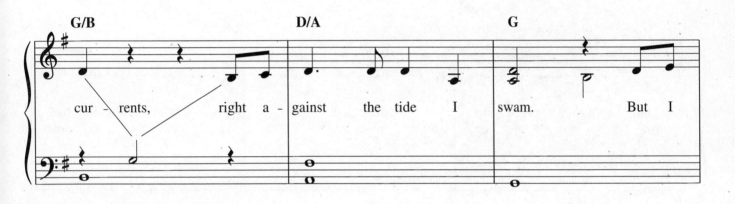

cur - rents, right a - gainst the tide I swam. But I

float - ed with the ques - tion who will love me

as I am? Like an

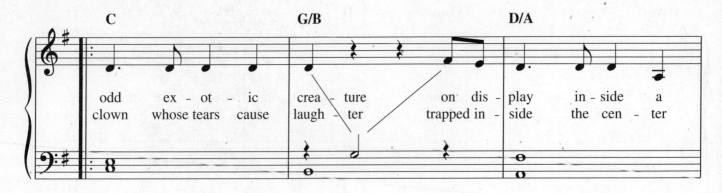

odd ex - ot - ic crea - ture on dis - play in - side a
clown whose tears cause laugh - ter trapped in - side the cen - ter

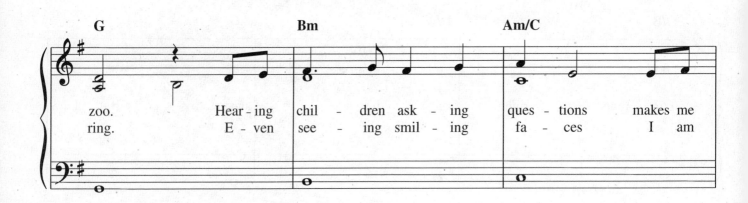

zoo. Hear - ing chil - dren ask - ing ques - tions makes me
ring. E - ven see - ing smil - ing fa - ces I am

ask some ques - tions too. Could we bend the laws of
lone - ly pon - der - ing. Who would want to join this

na - ture? Could a li - on love a lamb? Who could
mad - ness? Who would change my mon - o - gram? Who will

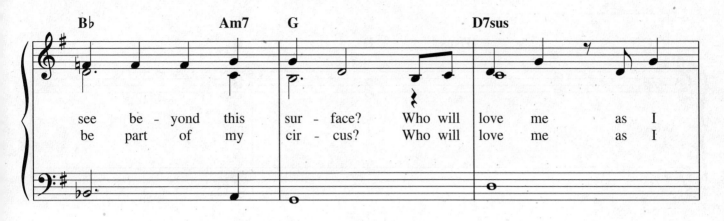

B♭ **Am7** **G** **D7sus**

see be - yond this sur - face? Who will love me as I
be part of my cir - cus? Who will love me as I

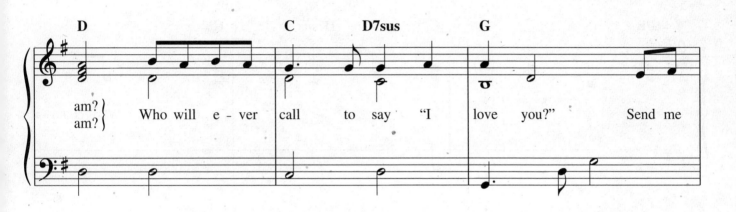

D **C** **D7sus** **G**

am? } Who will e - ver call to say "I love you?" Send me
am? }

C **D** **G** **C** **D**

flow - ers or a tel - e - gram? Who could proud - ly stand be -

Em7 **Bm/D** 1. **C** **Dsus** **D**

side me? Who will love me as I am? Like a

2.

| C | | D7sus | D | G |

love me as I am?

| G/B | C | D7sus | G |

Who could

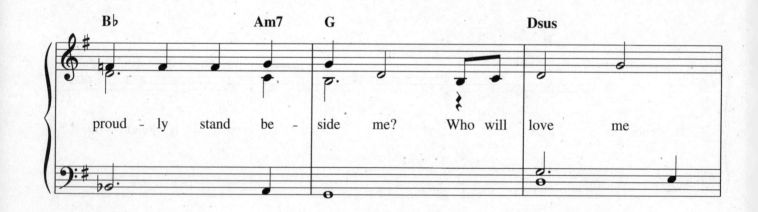

| Bb | Am7 | G | | Dsus |

proud - ly stand be - side me? Who will love me

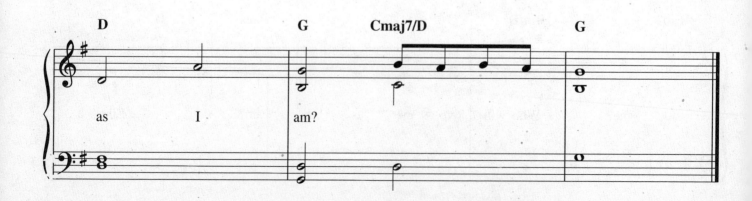

| D | G | Cmaj7/D | G |

as I am?

WITH A SONG IN MY HEART

from SPRING IS HERE

Words by LORENZ HART
Music by RICHARD RODGERS

With a song in my heart.

I be-hold your a-dor-a-ble face,   Just a song at the

start, _____   But it soon is a hymn to your grace.

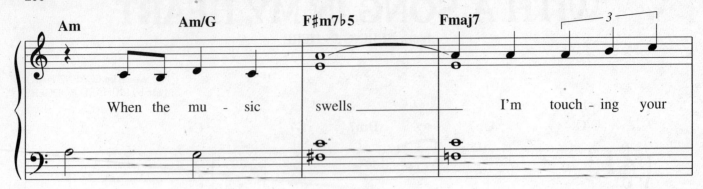

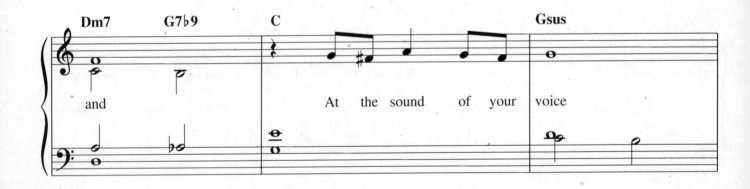

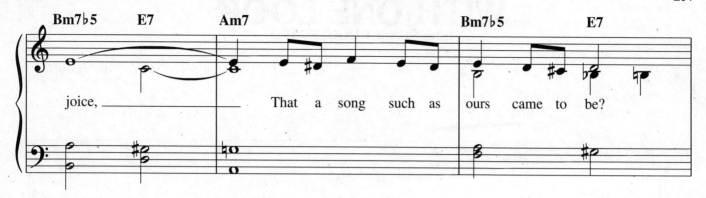

joice, _____ That a song such as ours came to be?

But I al - ways knew _____ I would live life

through, _____ With a song in my heart for

you. you.

WITH ONE LOOK
from SUNSET BOULEVARD

Music by ANDREW LLOYD WEBBER
Lyrics by DON BLACK and CHRISTOPHER HAMPTON,
with contributions by AMY POWERS

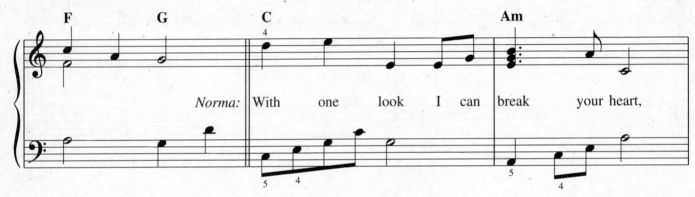

Norma: With one look I can break your heart,

with one look I play ev - ery part.

I can make your sad heart sing, with one

look you'll know all you need to know. With one smile I'm the

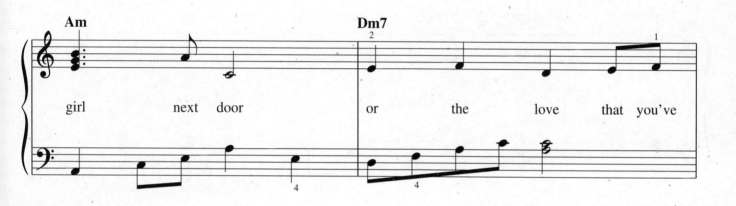

girl next door or the love that you've

hun - gered for. When I speak it's with my

soul I can play an - y role. No

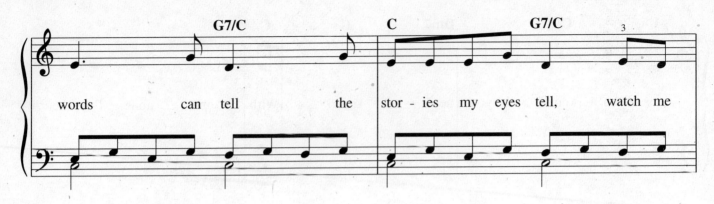

words can tell the stor-ies my eyes tell, watch me

when I frown, you can't write that down. You

know I'm right, it's there in black and white, when I

look your way you'll hear what I say. Yes, with one look I put

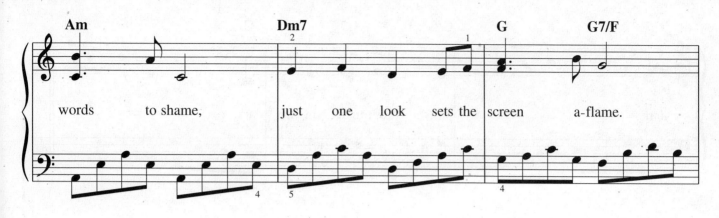

words to shame, just one look sets the screen a-flame.

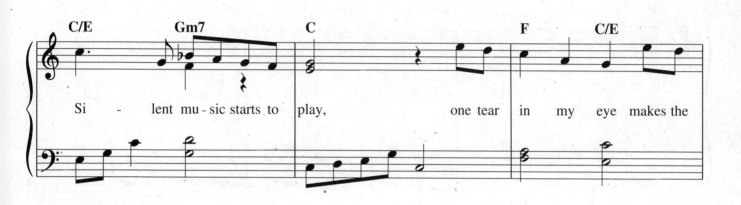

Si - lent mu - sic starts to play, one tear in my eye makes the

whole world cry. With one look they'll for - give the past,

they'll re - joice I've re - turned at last to my peo - ple in the

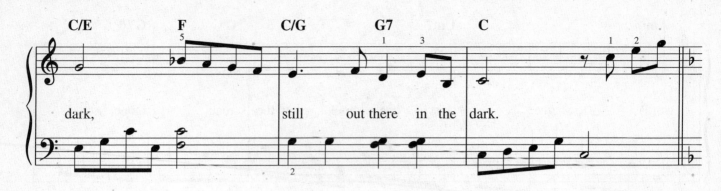

dark,   still   out there   in the   dark.

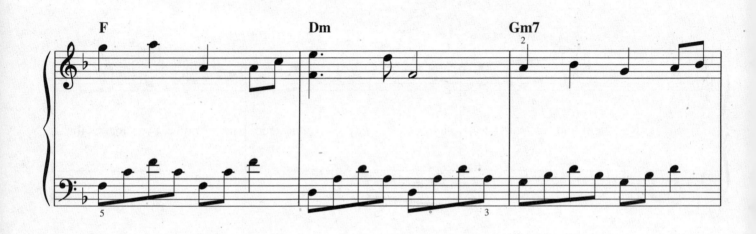

Si - lent mu-sic starts to play.   With one

look you'll know   all you   need   to know.   With   one   look   I'll ig-

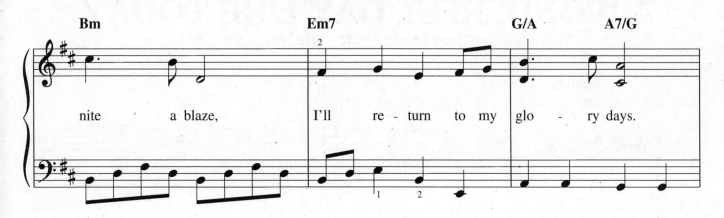

Bm　　　　　Em7　　　　　G/A　　　A7/G

nite　　a blaze,　　I'll re - turn to my glo - ry days.

D/F♯　　　Am　　　　D　　　　G(add9)

They'll　　say Nor-ma's back at　last.　　This time I am stay-ing, I'm

mf

G6　　　　　G　　　　　　Em

stay-ing for good,　　I'll be　back where I was born to　be,

f

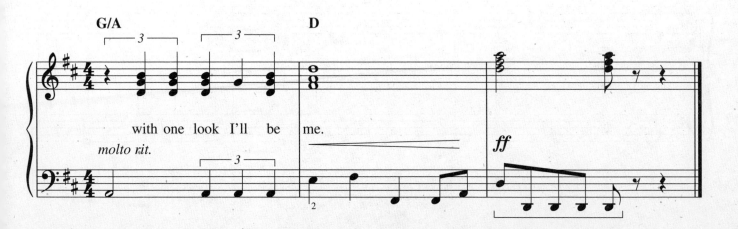

G/A　　　　　D

with one look I'll be　me.

molto rit.　　　　　　　*ff*

A WONDERFUL DAY LIKE TODAY

from THE ROAR OF THE GREASEPAINT - THE SMELL OF THE CROWD

Words and Music by LESLIE BRICUSSE
and ANTHONY NEWLEY

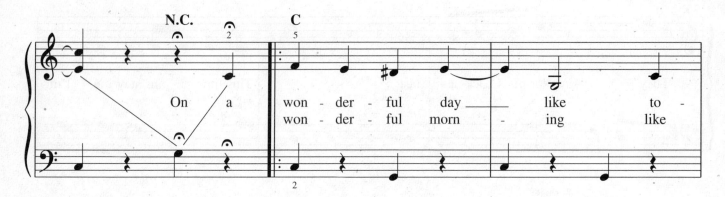

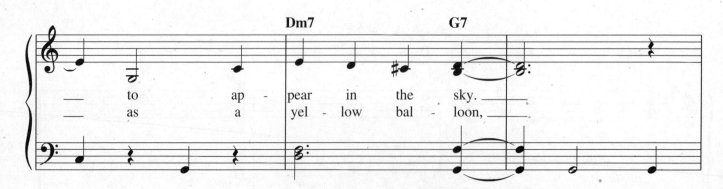

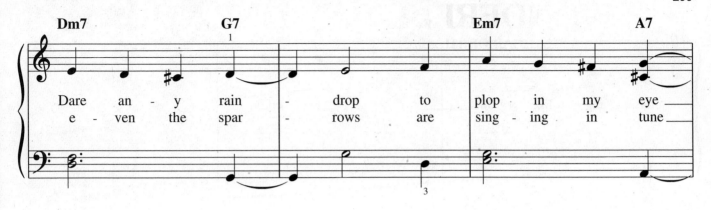

Dare an - y rain - drop to plop in my eye
e - ven the spar - rows are sing - ing in tune

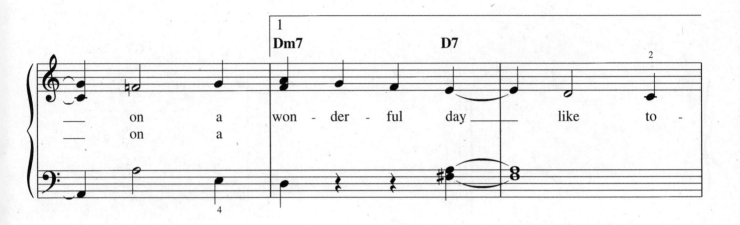

on a won-der-ful day like to-
on a

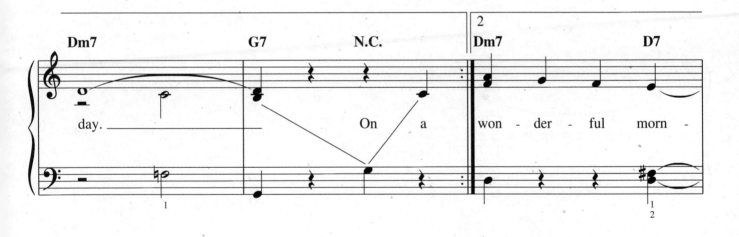

day. On a won-der-ful morn -

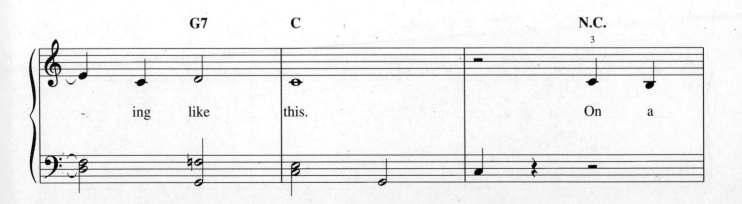

- ing like this. On a

morn - ing like this _____ I could kiss ev - 'ry -

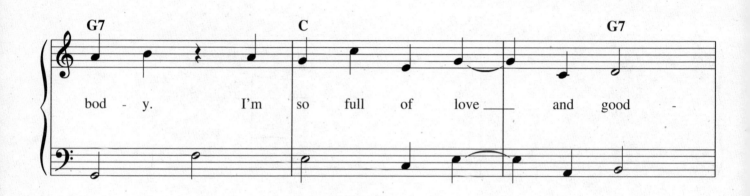

bod - y. I'm so full of love _____ and good -

will. _____ Let me say fur - ther - more _____

_____ I'd a - dore ev - 'ry - bod - y to

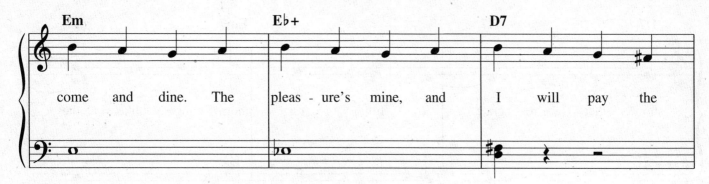

come and dine. The pleas-ure's mine, and I will pay the

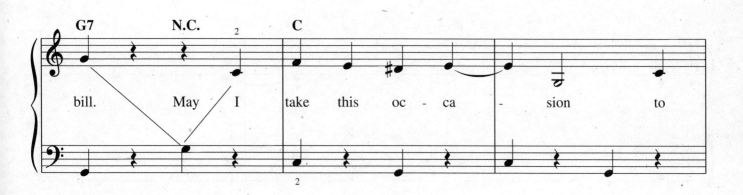

bill. May I take this oc - ca - sion to

say ____ that the whole hu - man race ____

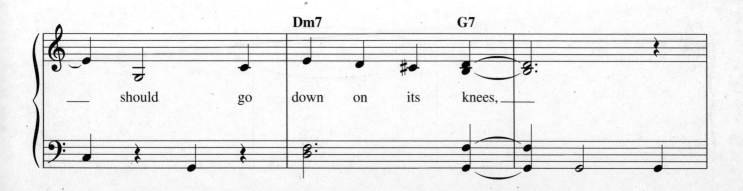

____ should go down on its knees, ____

show that we're grate - ful for morn - ings like these,

for the world's in a won - der - ful

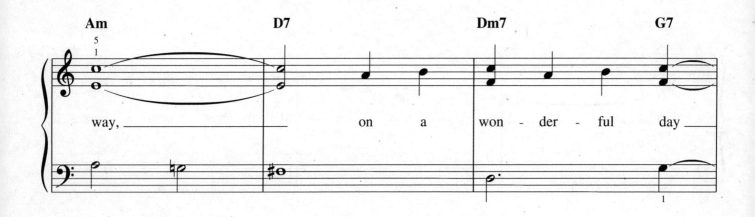

way, on a won - der - ful day

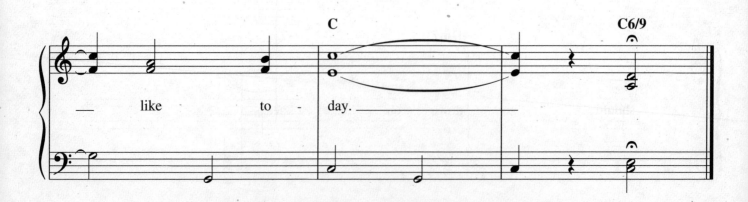

like to - day.

YOU'LL NEVER WALK ALONE

from CAROUSEL

Lyrics by OSCAR HAMMERSTEIN II
Music by RICHARD RODGERS

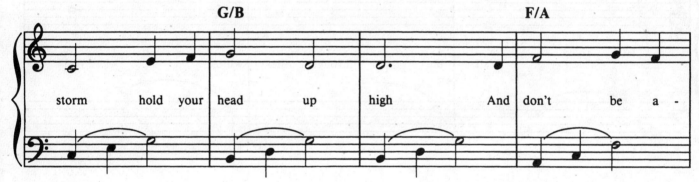

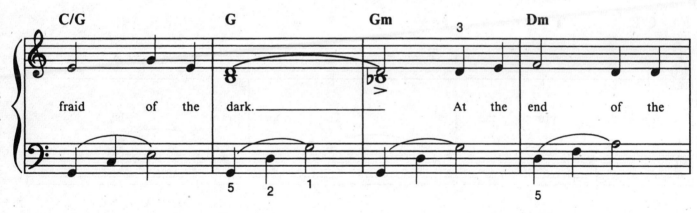

*Played throughout

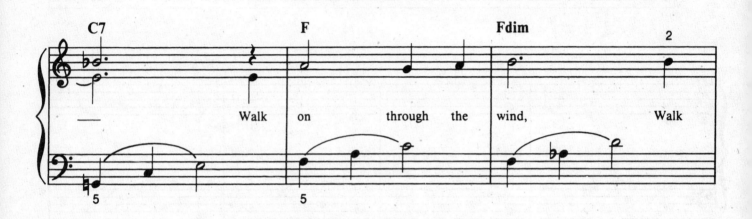

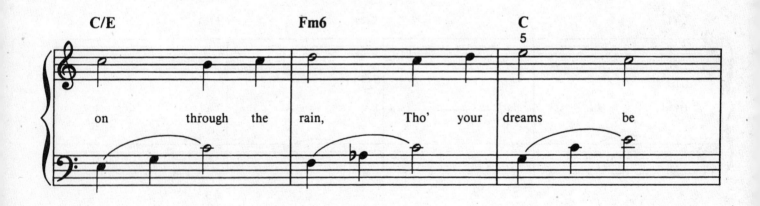

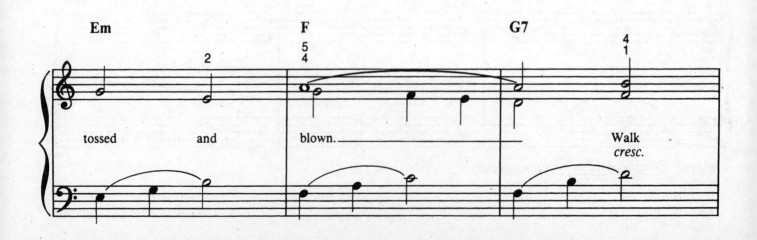

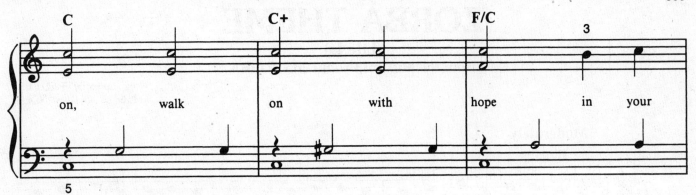

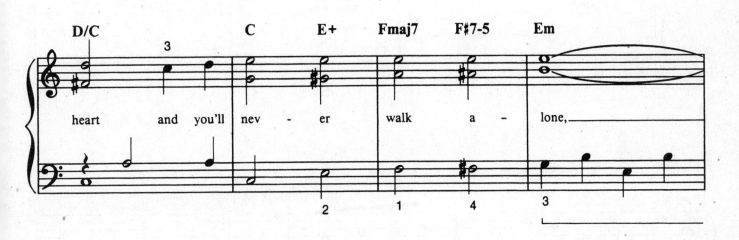

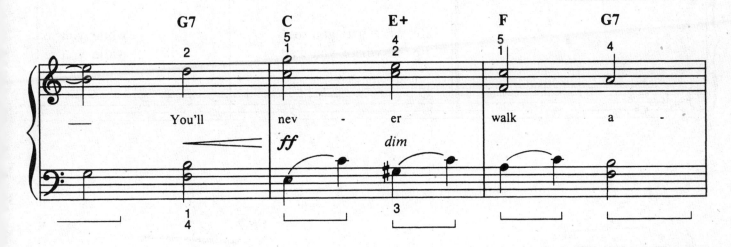

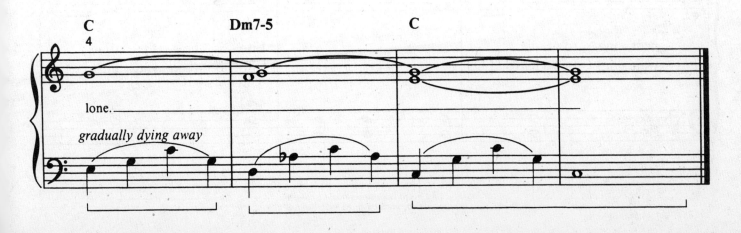

ZORBÁ THEME

(Life Is)
from the Musical Production ZORBÁ

Lyrics by FRED EBB
Music by JOHN KANDER

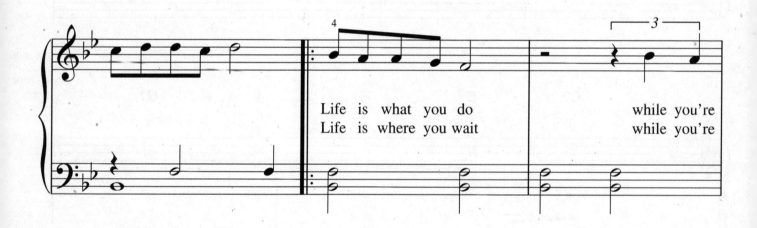

Life is what you do
Life is where you wait

while you're
while you're

wait - ing to die.
wait - ing to leave.

Life is how the time
Life is where you grin

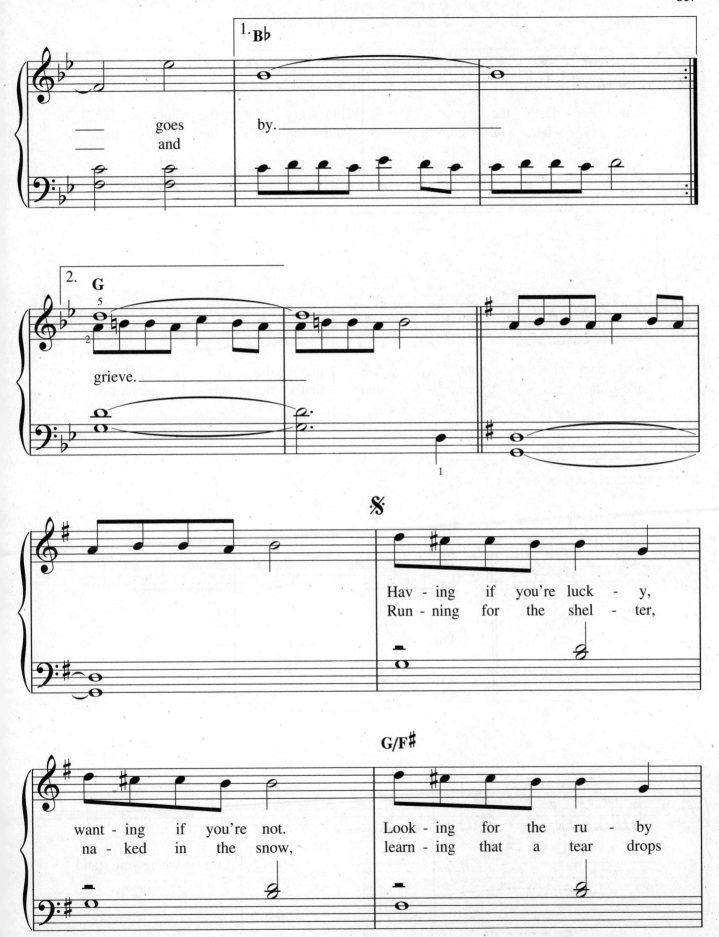

un - der - neath the rot.
an - y - where you go.

Hun - gry for the pi - laf in
Find - ing it's the mud that

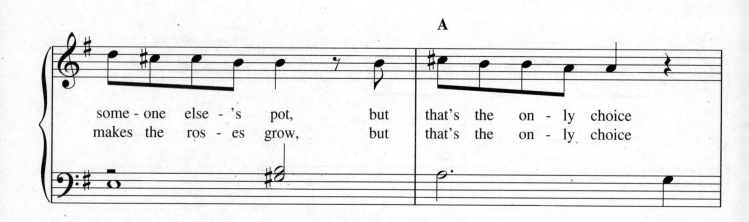

some - one else - 's pot,
makes the ros - es grow,

but
but

that's the on - ly choice
that's the on - ly choice

To Coda

you've
you

got!
know.

Life is where you stand

Life is what you feel ___ till you

can't feel at all. ___ Life is where you fly ___

___ and fall. ___

5

D.S. al Coda

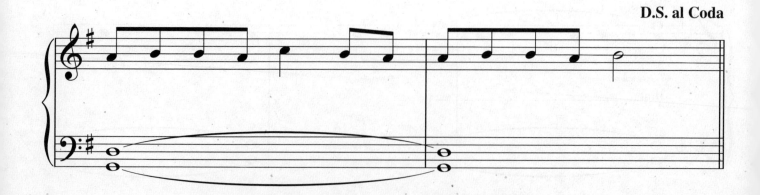

CODA

Freely
Fm7

This   is   how   the   time

Moderately
B♭

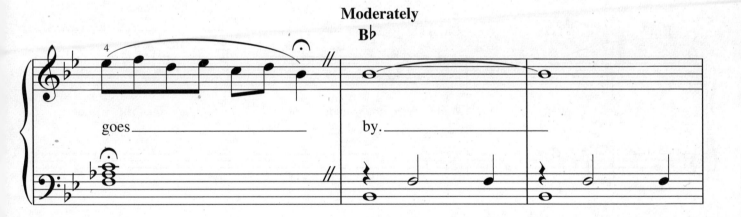

goes_____   by._____

accel. al fine

YOUNGER THAN SPRINGTIME

from SOUTH PACIFIC

Lyrics by OSCAR HAMMERSTEIN II
Music by RICHARD RODGERS

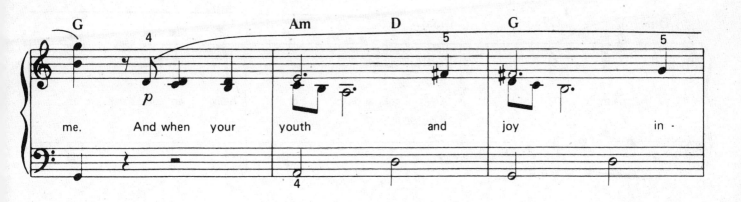

now they do,   then,

Young-er than spring - time am I, Gay - er than laugh - ter

am I, An - gel and lov - er, heav - en and earth am

I   with you!